SCIENCE ON THE MARCH

UNIT TEN

EARTH AND UNIVERSE

The 250-feet steerable radio telescope at Jodrell Bank Experimental Station, University of Manchester. The Consulting Engineers for the project were Messrs. Husband and Co., Sheffield, and the photograph is reproduced by permission of the Director of the Jodrell Bank Experimental Station.

SCIENCE ON THE MARCH

UNIT TEN

EARTH AND UNIVERSE

John A. Clark
Frederick L. Fitzpatrick
Edith Lillian Smith
Charles H. Dobinson

LONGMANS

LONGMANS, GREEN AND CO LTD
6 & 7 CLIFFORD STREET LONDON W1
THIBAULT HOUSE THIBAULT SQUARE CAPE TOWN
605–611 LONSDALE STREET MELBOURNE C1

LONGMANS, GREEN AND CO INC
55 FIFTH AVENUE NEW YORK 3

LONGMANS, GREEN AND CO
20 CRANFIELD ROAD TORONTO 16

ORIENT LONGMANS PRIVATE LTD
CALCUTTA BOMBAY MADRAS
DELHI HYDERABAD DACCA

First published in Great Britain 1958

This Unit has been adapted from part of SCIENCE ON THE MARCH by John A. Clark, Frederick L. Fitzpatrick and Edith Lillian Smith, published in the U.S.A. by the Houghton Mifflin Company. The adaptation has been made and a certain amount of new material added by C. H. Dobinson, M.A., B.Sc., Professor of Education in the University of Reading.

The first twelve Units of SCIENCE ON THE MARCH are:

1. The Air and You.
2. Water and Life.
3. The Weather and the Earth.
4. Life and Food.
5. Health.
6. Energy and Engines.
7. Hearing and Seeing.
8. Electric Currents.
9. Magnets and Electric Power.
10. Earth and Universe.
11. Birth and Growth.
12. Heating and Cooling.

The illustrations on the inside covers of this Unit are reproduced by permission from the end-papers of *The New Age Encyclopaedia* published by Wm. Collins Sons & Co., Ltd.

Made and Printed in Great Britain by Butler & Tanner Ltd, Frome and London

CONTENTS OF UNIT TEN

EARTH AND UNIVERSE

The Minneapolis Star & Tribune Co.

FIGURE 1. The total eclipse of the Sun of June 30th, 1954, photographed at Minneapolis, U.S.A.

Earth and Universe

Of all the branches of Science, the first to arouse the interest of man was astronomy, the study of the stars. No doubt the need to find some way of measuring time was partly responsible for this. Days could be counted, but how could years be measured ? And how could the day be divided up ? It is difficult for us in the modern world, who regard a wristwatch and clock as everyday objects, to think back to a world when man had invented no satisfactory device for measuring time. Yet the first clock that would keep accurate time on board ship was invented less than 200 years ago.

Thousands of years before then, early man must have noticed that every morning the sun rose in the eastern part of the sky and set in the western part in the evening. He must have noticed, too, that the stars as well as the moon move across the night sky in regular paths. Thus the sun could give time by day and the stars by night. Man long ago found out too that the paths of sun and stars across the heavens changed with the seasons of the year. In summer the sun is high in the heaven at mid-day. Do you know in what month the " Plough " (or, if you live in the southern hemisphere, the " Southern Cross ") is highest in the heavens at midnight ?

The ancient Chinese, Egyptians and Greeks all made very careful studies of the stars and gave names to groups of them. By A.D. 100 the Greeks had made a catalogue of over 1000 fixed stars. But even the ablest of their scientists (except for a very few) thought that the sun and stars all went round the earth. Some of the Greek knowledge was handed on to the Romans, but when the Roman Empire was destroyed most of this science was lost to western Europe for over a thousand years.

Then, quite suddenly, astronomy was on the march again. The thoughts of a Polish priest named Nicholas Kopernik turned man's idea of the universe inside out. His book, published in 1543, claimed that the earth went round the sun! About sixty years later the invention of the telescope enabled man to see far more than he had ever seen before. Since that time new knowledge has accumulated by leaps and bounds. And you will read in this book of new instruments, like the radio telescope, that have made it possible for us to record the movement of stars which are quite invisible.

Problem A: **HOW IMPORTANT TO OUR LIVES IS THE SUN?**

The sun does not look the same as the stars. But astronomers know that the sun really is a star. Because it appears so bright to us we might well suppose that it is one of the largest stars. But astronomers know that many stars are very much larger. It is only because we are so much nearer to the sun than to other stars that this particular star looks so big to us. Indeed, the earth and all the other planets make a little "family" round the sun that we call the *solar* (or sun) *system*. How important to us on the earth is this sun?

Courtesy Librarie Hachette

FIGURE 2. The Solar System ; or the sun and the planets. Can you find the earth and name all the other planets ?

Problem A : **How important to our lives is the Sun ?**

Question 1. **How does your life depend upon the Sun ?**

What do you need for life ? Among other things you need food, water, warmth, and light. Imagine any one of these missing, and you will realize that you could not remain alive. Let us recall how we depend upon the sun for all these essentials of life.

In Unit Four on LIFE AND FOOD you learned that we owe all our food to green plants and that plants owe their ability to make food to the energy of the sun. In Unit Six on ENERGY AND ENGINES you learned that without the energy of the sun to lift water from the seas and oceans there would soon be no rain and therefore no water on the dry land. And, of course, without the sun there would be no natural warmth, or natural light either (except a very little from the other stars). Even the coal and oil that we burn owe their origin to the sun for they were formed from the remains of plants and animals that had their warmth and their light from the sun millions of years ago.

Everyone knows that the sun's rays give heat, but have you tried the effect of the direct rays of the sun on a thermometer ? Place one thermometer in direct sunlight and another in the shade, being sure that the other conditions are similar. Keep a record of the temperatures, making observations every two minutes.

How much did the sun raise the temperature in ten minutes ?

Why would it not be scientific to place one thermometer outdoors and the other indoors ?

Repeat the experiment with both thermometers indoors in a fairly cool room with closed windows. Put one thermometer near the window in the sun's rays, and the other also near the window but shielded from the sun's rays by a sheet of brown paper. Compare these results with the previous ones.

Can you, now, as a result of these experiments, explain why people who record the weather have very special boxes, without glass, in which to keep their thermometers ?

FIGURE 3. A great prominence which appeared beyond the sun's surface on June 14th, 1946. See also Figure 12.

Courtesy Mount Wilson Observatory

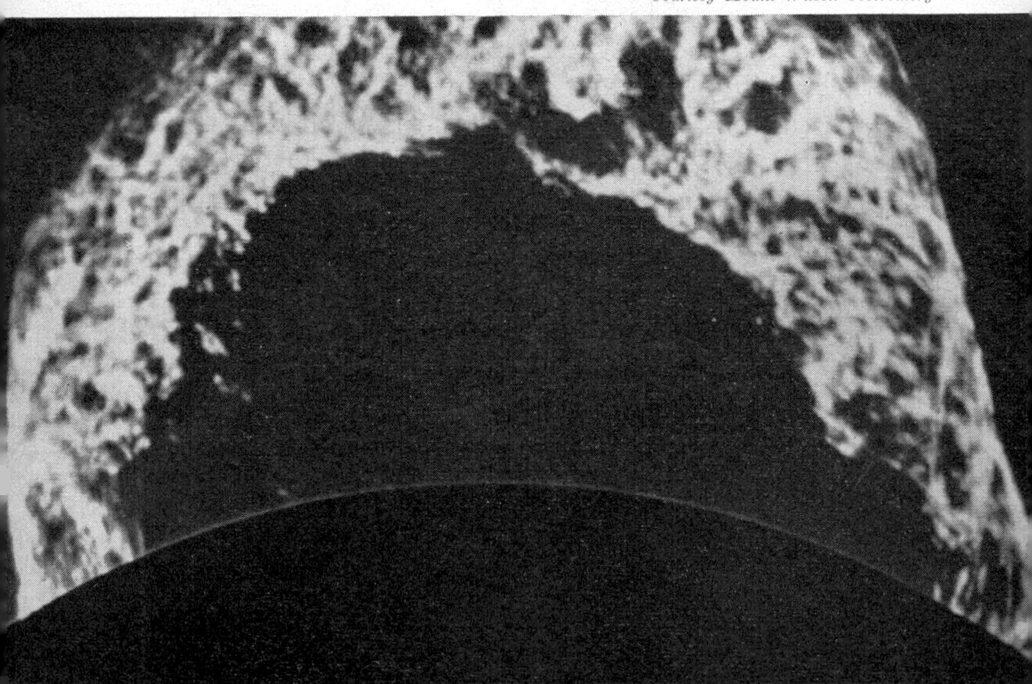

The sun is hot; so hot that it is impossible for us to realize what such a high temperature must mean. We know, however, that if the temperature of the earth were raised to that of the interior of the sun, then seas, plants, animals, metals and even rocks would no longer be solid or liquid but *gas.* So you see why astronomers believe that the whole of the sun, even its very centre, must be gas.

Scientists call the outermost layers of the sun its "atmosphere." These layers, about four thousand miles thick, show a ring of rosy red during a total eclipse of the sun. From this atmosphere clouds of glowing gas sweep up and around in ever-changing masses. By means of a telescope and a special kind of camera these amazing happenings can be filmed. Sometimes whirling areas of gas are associated with small dark marks on the sun's surface and these are called "sun-spots." Also from time to time flaming red streamers form and shoot outward, sometimes reaching heights of hundreds of thousands of miles.

Still farther away from the sun stretches the sun's corona (which means "crown"). This can be seen

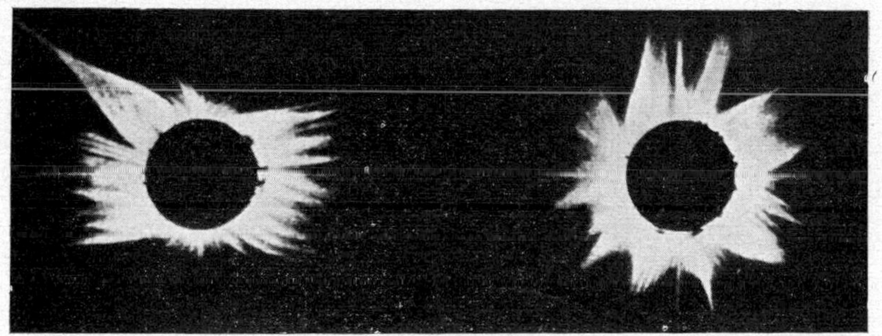

Courtesy Yerkes Observatory

FIGURE 4. The sun's corona. The photograph on the left shows the wings at a time when sun-spots were at their minimum. The photograph on the right shows more uniform spread when sun-spots were at their maximum.

in total eclipses as a beautiful pearly halo extending into space for millions of miles.

Years ago the sun's corona could be studied only at times of eclipse of the sun, but nowadays there is an instrument which enables the corona to be kept under continual observation.

The shape and the extent of the crown vary greatly according to the number and area of spots on the sun's surface at the time. We do not yet know why this should be but it may have something to do with the sun's magnetism. But we do know that short wireless waves are affected at times by the " spottiness " of the sun and it is probable that the sun-spots slightly alter the sun's effect on the earth in other ways too.

" Sun stuff at its thinnest " is how one astronomer has described the gases that make the sun's corona. Their temperature is thought to be over 100 times hotter than the temperature of the surface of the sun—which is about 10,000° C. Soon we shall know more about things that can happen in the sun's corona, as in 1957 British scientists at Harwell produced a temperature of about 5,000,000° C.

SOME THINGS YOU MAY CARE TO DO

1. Smoke a piece of glass in a candle flame or other smoky flame until it is well covered. Use it to look at the sun. Can you see any spots on its surface? *Caution :* Never look directly at the sun without this protection, or the similar protection given you by an exposed film negative that is uniformly black—you may need more than one layer of film to protect your eyes. At the time of the last partial eclipse visible in England many people damaged their eyes through looking at the sun without proper protection.

2. With a Meccano or similar construction set, fix up an apparatus like that shown in Figure 5. Then draw the blind in a sunny room and arrange for a beam of the sun's light to pass through the telescope. Quite a small telescope will serve and if there are any spots on the sun's face at the time you will be able to see them on the white paper screen. The draw tube must be pushed in and out until the picture of the sun looks quite sharp at the edge. Otherwise you may suppose that any little marks caused by specks of dust on the lens are sun-spots!

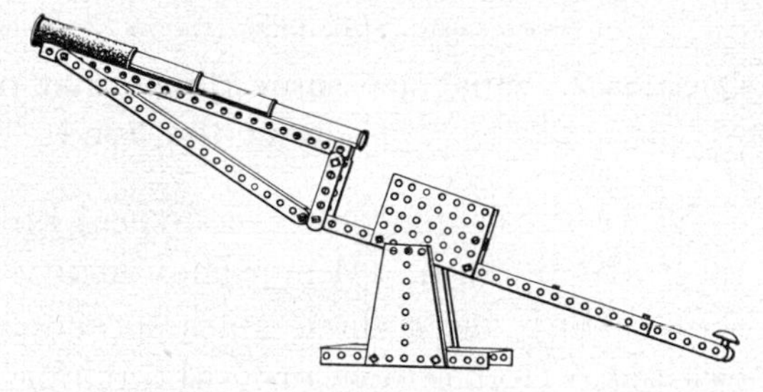

FIGURE 5. This simple support for a telescope made by a boy of 13 enabled him to record sun-spots and to use a cheap box camera to photograph the sun.

3. Using a magnetic compass, keep a careful record of the positions in the sky in which the sun appears (*a*) to rise, (*b*) to set. Keep this record for at least a month. You will need a degree scale which you can make on paper from your protractor as the ordinary small magnetic compass does not give small enough divisions for you to make accurate measurements. Can you find out why the sun appears red at rising and setting and why you can then generally look directly at it without discomfort? If ever you are able to see the sun through thick cloud, fog or mist, give a drawing and make notes on the difference in its appearance and effect.

4. Demonstrate the heat of the sun by lighting a small fire with a convex lens, or "burning glass." Then read about the burning glasses used by Archimedes.

Question 2. **What are some things that men have found out about the Sun?**

Nowadays scientists use several kinds of instruments to study the sun. When they study it through a telescope, they use a dark glass screen, and also a special eye-piece that allows only about one-tenth of the light and heat to pass through the telescope tube. Without this eye-piece the dark glass could be splintered by the concentrated heat and the observer's eye might be permanently damaged before he realized what had happened. *So never look at the sun directly through a telescope unless you have both the dark glass and the special eye-piece.*

The disc of the sun, when studied in this way, appears to be mottled. Very tiny white patches are separated by dark areas. These white patches used to be called "rice-grains" but nowadays are generally called "granules"—meaning "little grains." But they are not really very small, for each is about 900 miles wide. They appear to be always on the move and jostling one another. Also they seem to gather in extra numbers in the region of sun-spots, especially where two or more sun-spots are very close together. We do not know what these granules are, but they may be regions where swirling columns of gas come up to the sun's surface from within. Each granule has a life-time of only a few minutes.

FIGURE 6. Photograph of the great sunspot of April 7th, 1947. Can you estimate what proportion of the sun's disc was taken up by spots on that date?

Courtesy Mount Wilson & Palomar Observatories

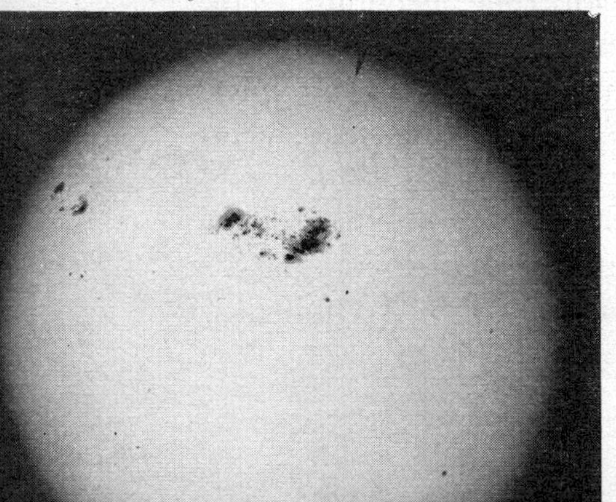

The Chinese, without any telescopes to help them, had made records of spots on the sun's surface as long ago as A.D. 200. But they were not recorded in Europe until Galileo saw them through his telescope. His announcement created an uproar, not least in the Church of that time, for some people thought it would be irreligious to believe that the sun had blemishes, as this would suggest that there was something wrong with God's handiwork! But even unscientific people might occasionally have seen some spots on the sun's face if they had looked at the sun through thick haze, though this is only possible at a time when the spots are particularly large.

Can you now suggest how the Chinese observations may have been possible?

Since the time of Galileo, astronomers have given a good deal of attention to sun-spots. The invention recently of a number of new instruments enables us to know about even the magnetic properties of sun-spots, and also something about the gases that compose them. They seem to be great whirlpools of gas, probably swirling upwards from below what seems to us to be the "surface" of the sun.

FIGURE 7. This is a larger picture of the great sun-spot shown in Figure 6.

Courtesy Mount Wilson & Palomar Observatories

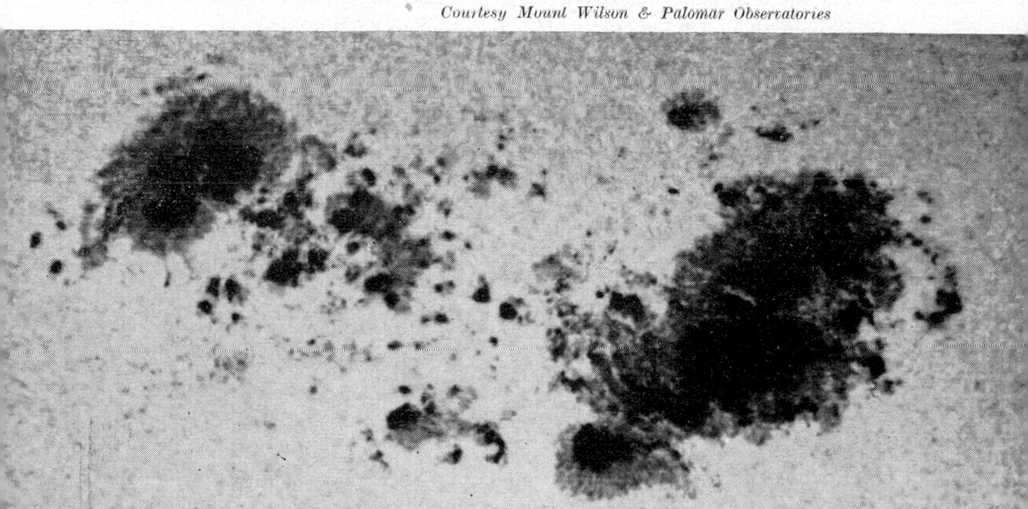

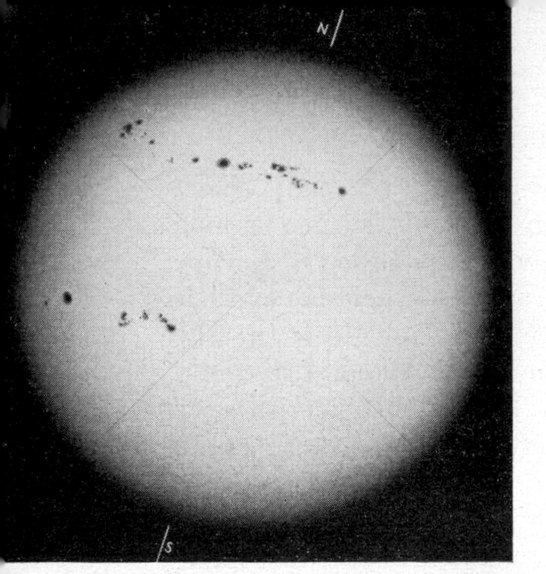

Courtesy Royal Greenwich Observatory

FIGURE 8. A photograph of the sun's disc at a time of considerable sun-spot activity, February 17th, 1956.

Sun-spots vary in size from minute " pores "—which are dark patches among the " granules "—to a huge area of 6000 million square miles covered by the great sun-spot of April 1947. The " pores " are often so small that they are hardly visible through huge telescopes. While some " pores " grow bigger and develop into proper sun-spots, others may disappear in a few hours.

One of the most interesting things about sun-spots is that the number of spots on the sun steadily increases and decreases in a fairly regular way. About every 11 years the sun has an extra large number of spots. We call this a period of *sun-spot maximum*. Then over a period of about 7 or $7\frac{1}{2}$ years the number of spots gradually gets smaller and smaller till we have a period of *sun-spot minimum*. Then, 3 or 4 years after this, we have a maximum again. The 11-year period is an average of spans which have varied between 9 and 13 years, but usually the period between two maxima is roughly 11 years. From this graph you can see when the last maximum occurred, and when the next is likely.

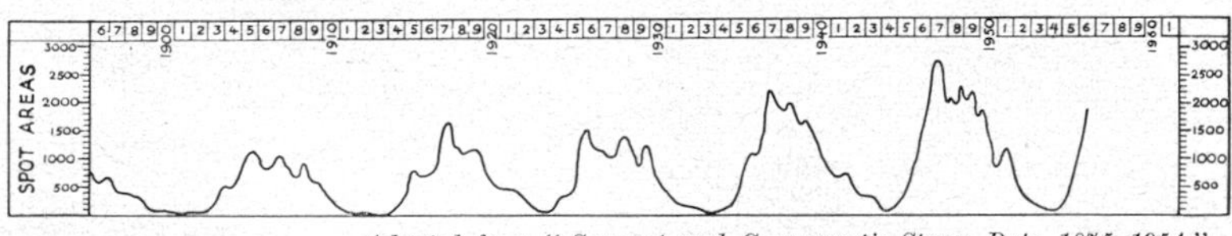

Adapted from " Sunspot and Geomagnetic-Storm Data 1875–1954," by permission of the Controller of H.M.S.O.

FIGURE 9. This graph shows you the variation in sun-spot areas over the past 60 years. What things does this graph tell you ?

Now look back at Figure 4 and compare the sun's corona at these two stages. You will see that at sun-spot maximum the sun's corona is more uniform than when the spots are at a minimum ; but it does not extend so far into space. The heat we receive from the sun is believed to be slightly greater at periods of sun-spot maximum and this is said to cause greater evaporation over the oceans and so higher rainfall in some regions. This higher rainfall has been said to affect those semi-desert regions where locusts breed. By increasing the green food supply, the higher rainfall brings about an increase in the number of locusts. In the following years when the rainfall is less, the green plants fail to grow and the locusts migrate in billions. Such migrations cause the plagues known in Egypt in ancient times and still known today in other parts of Africa. Whether in fact there is any such connection between the sun-spot period and locust plagues we do not yet know. A great deal more very careful keeping of records needs to be done. You will remember from past Units that scientists are always very careful indeed not to make up their minds about anything until they are absolutely sure about the facts. So, although it is possible that the varying number of spots on the sun *may* affect our weather, and consequently a lot of other things too, we can only say that *we are not sure*.

But we are sure of one way in which sun-spots affect us on earth. In regions of sun-spot activity there often arise on the surface of the sun very bright outbursts or " flares " of glowing hydrogen. These are rarely brilliant enough to be seen with an ordinary telescope but they can be seen plainly in photographs taken in hydrogen light. These flares on the sun's surface interfere with radio waves and cause radio

Paul Popper, Ltd.

FIGURE 10. A photograph from Norway of Aurora Borealis. This is a shimmering band of coloured light with many shades of semi-transparent greens, purples, and reds and with dark vertical patches running rhythmically along the folds of moving curtain.

"fade out." They lead to displays of the beautiful aurora borealis or "northern lights." They affect a compass needle so much that navigators talk of a "magnetic storm." On 24th February, 1956, radio contact with a British submarine was lost for so long that the B.B.C. and the newspapers reported that a disaster was feared. Only some hours afterwards was it discovered that there had been at the time severe radio disturbance and later this was found to be associated with flares accompanying a giant sun-spot.

THE SUN'S ROTATION

By daily observation of the face of the sun and by looking particularly at sun-spots and other special markings, astronomers found out that the sun is spinning, just like the earth, as it moves through space. But the sun takes much longer to turn round than does the earth: the period at the equator of the sun is 25 days. When we observe the sun's rotation from the earth, it appears to take $27\frac{1}{4}$ days—the difference is due to the fact that the earth during this time is itself moving on its orbit round the sun.

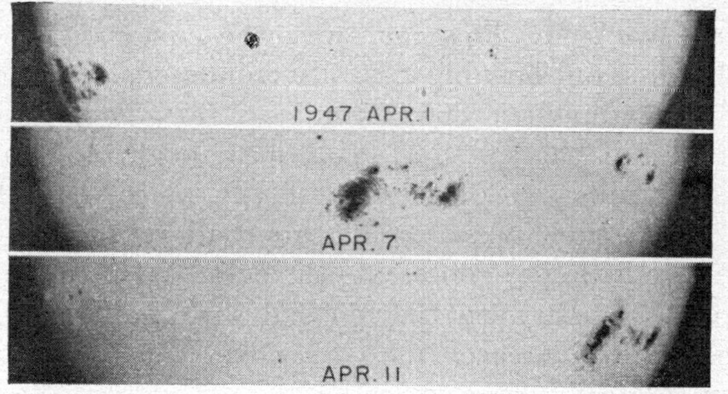

Courtesy Mount Wilson & Palomar Observatories

FIG. 11. These three photographs show the position on three days of the same sun-spot group as in Figures 6 and 7. What do they tell you about the rotation of the sun ?

MEASURING THE SUN

The next thing you may wish to know about the sun is its distance from the earth. How can men possibly tell what this is ? You have probably seen surveyors at work with measuring instruments. They are able to find out how far one hill-top is from another without actually travelling between them. They can tell the distance across a river without crossing it. Indeed, you may yourself know a simple method of doing this, and of measuring the height of a church steeple without having to climb it. Many Scouts and Guides are familiar with such methods.

Astronomers are surveyors of the sky. When they try to use the same methods that surveyors use on the earth, they meet with great difficulties. However, by using very delicate instruments, by being exceedingly careful, and by repeating the measurements over and over again, they have found that the sun is roughly 93,000,000 miles away from the earth. Do you know why the distance changes just a very little from day to day and why the earth is sometimes farther from the sun than at other times ?

Once we know how far away the sun is, it is not hard to find out how big it is. Astronomers have found that its diameter is 866,000 miles. Do you know the diameter of the earth? You may begin to realize the enormous size of the sun if you place a football and a pea side by side. The football represents the sun: the little pea represents the earth. On this scale the distance between the football and the pea ought to be slightly greater than a cricket pitch—actually about 72 feet.

Look at Figure 12. This gives us some idea of the different layers of the sun's atmosphere.

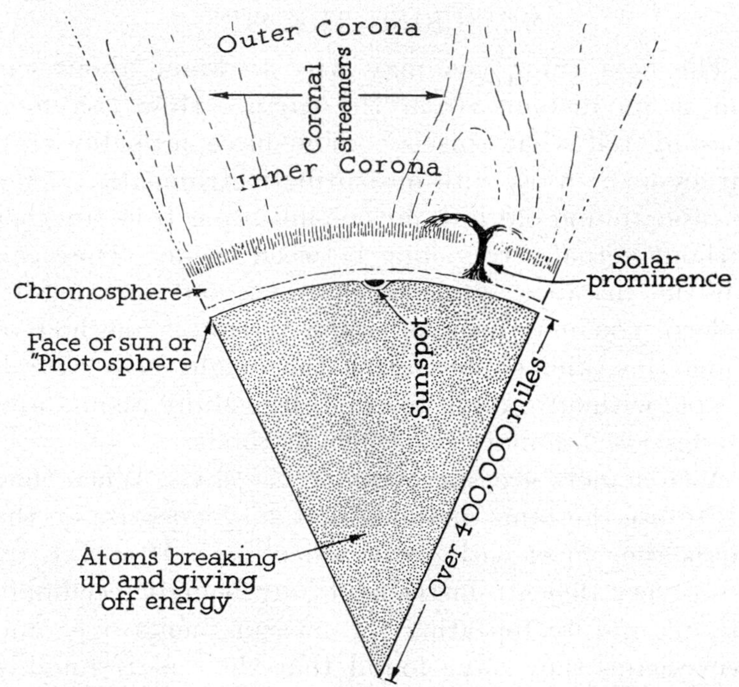

Based on Fig. 1·1 in Ellison: "The Sun and Its Influence," by permission of Routledge & Kegan Paul, Ltd.

FIGURE 12. This diagram shows the great difference in size between solar prominences and coronal streamers. The layer surrounding the face of the sun, called the chromosphere, appears as a ring of red light and consists mainly of hydrogen.

1. Make a scale model to represent the sun and the earth. Take an ordinary rubber balloon, preferably of an orange or yellow colour to represent the sun. Blow it up till it has a diameter of about 8 inches. Suppose that the sun's diameter is 800,000 miles (instead of 866,000). Work out the diameter of a model of the earth on the same scale, taking the earth's diameter as roughly 8000 miles. Then try to find a round object of the right size. Now suppose that the distance of the sun from the earth is 80,000,000 miles (instead of 93,000,000), and work out how far away one of your friends must stand with the model of the earth when you hold the balloon. In summer you may find a cricket pitch useful for this demonstration.

2. If you do not already know how to measure the height of a church spire or the width of a river without actually going up or across it, try to find out the method. Make a collection of such measurements, with diagrams and other details, in a notebook.

3. Read about Galileo and give a report to your class on his telescope, and his discovery of sun-spots.

4. Using apparatus like that in Figure 5, try to keep a series of records of anything you can see in the way of sun-spots over a period of some months. In which year is the next sun-spot maximum likely to occur ?

5. Refer to books on radio and see if they tell you anything about the interference due to sun-spots. What do they tell you about the effect of the various layers of the earth's atmosphere on radio waves ?

6. See what you can find, for a talk to your class, about the latest inventions for using the direct heat of the sun as a source of energy.

Question 3. **How does light show us the composition of the Sun ?**

Nowadays we can obtain light from candles, from oil, from burning gas, from ordinary electric lamps with filaments, from fluorescent tubes, from neon tubes, and so on. But for most of our lives we depend upon the light from the sun. Can we learn anything about it by experiment ?

If you allow a beam of sunlight to pass through a slit in a dark curtain and to fall on a glass prism, you will notice a band of colour. Arrange a white screen so that the band shows on it (see Figure 14). The colours blend into each other, but you should be able to distinguish at least six : violet, blue, green, yellow, orange and red. Some people distinguish a seventh colour, the very deep blue called indigo, between the violet and the blue. These colours side by side are called the " solar spectrum." Sometimes they are called " the colours of the rainbow," for raindrops act somewhat like glass prisms in breaking up the sunlight into separate colours.

FIGURE 13. Sir Isaac Newton used a slit in a curtain to investigate light.
Hulton Picture Library

If you want to remember the colours of the spectrum in the right order, one way is to take the letters of the unreal word VIBGYOR, which you can easily remember by saying it over to yourself a number of times.

Besides prisms and raindrops there are a number of

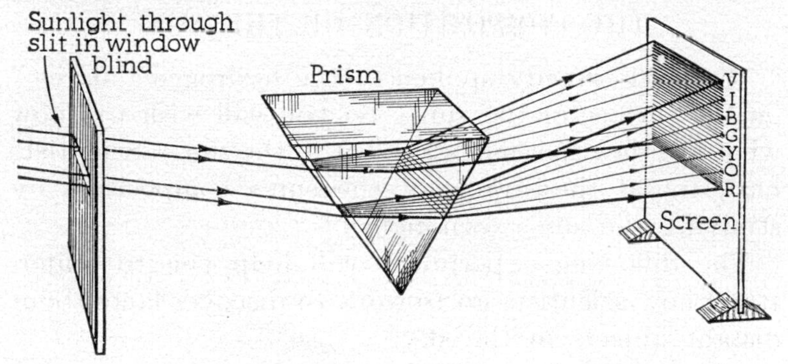

FIGURE 14. Producing a spectrum from sunlight.

other things, such as cut-glass tumblers or vases and the spray from a hose pipe, that can split the light from the sun into a number of colours. *Can you recall any times when you have seen glints of different colours from objects on which sunlight is falling?*

ULTRA-VIOLET RAYS

Besides the rays from the sun that give us light and heat, there are other waves, shorter waves, beyond the violet end of the spectrum. These tan our skin and have a chemical effect upon many plants and animals. These are called "ultra-violet rays," the word *ultra* being the Latin for *beyond*. They are of very great importance to us as being health-giving and destructive to bacteria. Unfortunately they are easily stopped in their passage through the air by dust and smoke, so very few of these rays penetrate the atmosphere of our great cities.

Ultra-violet rays help us to form in our own skin some of the vitamins we need. So you may care to read again about vitamins in Unit 4 on LIFE AND FOOD and Unit 5 on HEALTH.

We have already spoken of the hydrogen "flares" on the surface of the sun. So you will wish to know what are the other gases present in the sun. Scientists have found the secrets of the sun's composition by studying the sun's own light.

The following experiment will help you to understand how scientists go to work to discover facts about distant objects in the sky.

A lighted bunsen burner is adjusted to produce a clear blue flame. This flame is hot enough to cause many substances held in it to change to vapour. By means of pliers, hold a piece of copper in the flame. You cannot see the vapour, but you will notice that the flame changes colour. The new colour is due to the presence of copper vapour.

You may repeat the experiment with zinc and other things. If your teacher has a platinum wire which he can dip into solutions, you will be able to notice some very interesting colours in the flame if he uses the substances: common salt, saltpetre, calcium nitrate, strontium nitrate, barium nitrate. Record very carefully the colours you see. In this list there are two substances which turn the flame red, but the two shades of red are quite different. Remember that accurate observation is the beginning of all the work of a scientist, so see if you can

FIGURE 15. Contrast the flames of these two bunsen burners. The flame on the right is golden above the platinum wire which had previously been dipped into a solution of common salt.

find comparisons by which to fix the red colours in your mind—names such as flower-pot red or geranium-red.

If your teacher has no platinum wire, a porcelain rod will do almost as well. The important thing is to use something which will not itself give off vapour in the flame.

Now you should be able to answer the following question : *How may the flame test be used to detect the presence of an element ?*

HOW SCIENTISTS HAVE LEARNED WHAT IS IN THE SUN

This experiment shows that certain substances, when heated, glow with certain colours. Scientists began to wonder if they could tell what was in the sun by its colour. They decided that certain things were probably there, but this guess was not enough to satisfy them.

Scientists have found that no two substances, when heated very hot, give off light of exactly the same colour. While copper gives a beautiful shade of bluish-green, zinc gives a pale blue. You can see this colour if you throw a discarded dry battery into a fire, for these batteries contain zinc.

What we call one colour can be " spread out " by a prism into a wide *spectrum.* This shows us that one colour is really a mixture of several colours. Some scientists who make a study of such experiments can tell just what a substance is made of without seeing it. Thus, if you were to heat a piece of brass (which is made of copper and zinc) they could tell you at once from the colours they see in the spectrum coming from it that you had heated both copper and zinc.

In a similar way, by studying spectra, scientists can trace other elements such as iron, nickel, manganese, chromium, sulphur, phosphorus, and carbon.

When a substance is heated very hot, not all of the colours of the rainbow appear in its spectrum. The spaces between the colours are dark. No two substances have the same colours or dark spaces in their spectra. When men look at the spectrum of a mixture of several very hot substances, they have to study all the dark spaces as well as the colours.

To the unaided eye the spectrum of sunshine shows no dark spaces. One colour seems to begin where the next leaves off. But, if the spectrum is made long enough, many dark spaces can be seen. They are so fine and narrow that they are called *lines* (see Figure 16). The usual name is Fraunhofer lines, after the German scientist who carefully studied and measured them in 1814. He mapped 576 lines and fixed their positions by letters and numbers ; you see the letters along the top of the band in Figure 16. The letters at the bottom indicate elements that correspond to certain dark lines ; thus Fe stands for the element iron (from the Latin word *ferrum* for *iron*) and Ca stands for calcium. The instrument used to spread out the light, so that both the bright colours and the dark

FIGURE 16. The sun's spectrum expanded by a spectroscope. This enables dark lines to be seen among the bright colours. Scientists have found out what substances cause the dark lines and so are able to tell what substances are present in the sun's atmosphere.

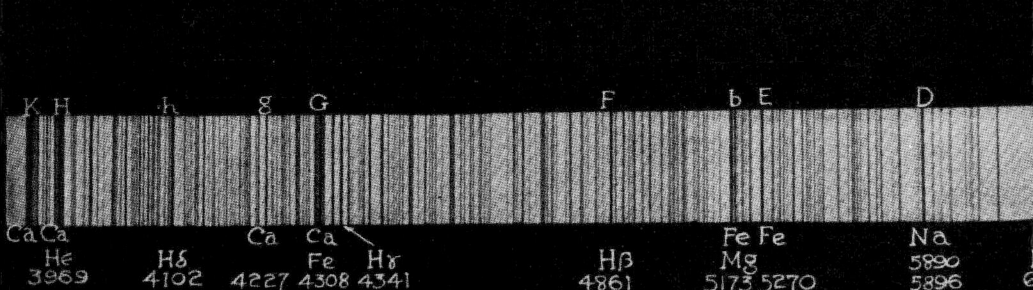

lines can be seen, is called a *spectroscope* (*scope* means *seeing*). It works on the same principle as the prism in Figure 14, but it also has lenses and measuring scales.

Anyone can look into a spectroscope and see beautiful colours and dark lines, but only scientists who have made a special study of the spectrum can tell what these mean. Such scientists have told us that the sun contains much the same elements as the earth. For example, it contains iron, sodium (a part of our common salt), calcium (a part of limestone and chalk and many other rocks), carbon (which forms part of all living matter), and hydrogen (a part of water).

Nearly one hundred years ago a man found a substance in the sun that was not known on the earth. The story of this discovery is an interesting one, for it shows how the work of many scientists of different countries may be necessary before an addition to the world's knowledge is possible. First came Wollaston, an Englishman. In 1802 he noticed the dark lines in the spectrum. Then Fraunhofer the German studied them. Later, a French astronomer journeyed to India to observe a total eclipse of the sun. By using a spectroscope, a fairly new instrument at that time, he saw an orange line that had not been noticed before. Further study convinced him that this line showed something in the sun that was unknown on earth. Scientists in other countries agreed with him and so the new substance was named *helium* from *helios*, the Greek word for *sun*.

Still later, the spectroscope showed that helium existed in certain other stars. Then after a few years a scientist noticed the same line in the spectrum of the gases flaming from Vesuvius. So this gas did exist on earth too, and not in stars only. Then Sir William Ramsay in England found traces of the gas, first in certain minerals and finally in the air. After that, American scientists found considerable quantities of helium in the natural gas from oil wells in some parts of the United States. So you can see that the study of the sun, 93 million miles away from us, has led to our discovering a gas existing on our own earth.

SOME THINGS THAT YOU MAY CARE TO DO

1. If your teacher can let you look through a direct-vision spectroscope (which consists of glass prisms fixed together in a tube), handle the instrument with care, and see how many colours you can see.

2. See if you can produce a spectrum by using a prism and some kind of artificial light.

3. Prepare a talk for your class on "Colours in the Sky." (Turn to Unit 7, HEARING AND SEEING, page 70.)

4. Make your own rainbow indoors. (You will find instructions on how to do this in Unit 7, page 72.)

5. Perhaps a group of your class can prepare a talk on ultra-violet light from the sun, every member of the group taking a different part of the subject such as how ultra-violet light from the sun is recorded, how it affects photographic plates, how it affects human beings, how it affects plants on land and plants in lakes and plants in the sea, and how these aquatic plants affect the fish, and what is being done by cities to reduce the smoke that keeps ultra-violet rays from getting through to us.

6. Perhaps a group of you could give to your class a report on the different forms of light, natural and artificial. Include fireflies, glowworms, and phosphorescent fishes, as well as the light given by the sun, moon, stars, northern lights, neon tubes, gas mantles, and so on.

Problem B: HOW IMPORTANT IS THE MOON?

The moon is much the nearest of all our neighbours in the sky. Indeed it is so near that even with your naked eye you can see something of the light and dark areas of its surface. Quite a small pocket telescope, or a pair of field glasses, is usually sufficient to enable you to see some of the detail shown in Figure 17. Have you yourself ever seen the crater Tycho from which great tracks radiate? Through the great telescopes used by astronomers ranges of jagged mountains can be plainly seen. With the world's biggest telescope, the 200-inch one at Mount Palomar, the moon is as clear as it would be to the naked eye if it were only 24 miles away.

Because the moon follows the earth on its journey, it is called a *satellite* of the earth, from the Latin word meaning an "attendant." On October, 4th 1957, Russian scientists gave the earth its first *artificial* satellite, Sputnik I, the Russian word *sputnik* meaning a "companion." This was a remarkable achievement of mathematicians, scientists and engineers and it has opened up vast new possibilities whereby men can discover more about the nature of the earth's

Courtesy Mount Wilson & Palomar Observatories

FIGURE 17. A photograph of the full moon taken with the 100-inch telescope at Mount Wilson. Tycho is near the bottom of the photograph. On the front end-paper you can find the crater Copernicus: now find it on this photograph.

upper atmosphere, the sun and radiations from space.

This satellite was followed on November 3rd, 1957, by Sputnik II which weighed about half a ton. It circled the earth 2370 times, travelling a distance of over 60 million miles, before it re-entered the earth's atmosphere and burnt out on April 14th, 1958. The first American satellite was launched on January 31st, 1958.

These launchings were part of the activities of the International Geophysical Year 1957–8 when scientists from all nations worked together to find out more about the physical nature of the earth.

Problem B : How important is the Moon ?

Question 1. **What do we know about the Moon ?**

The sun shines with a dazzling light that can damage our eyes if we look directly at it. We cannot damage our eyes by looking at the moon, for it shines with a softer light. The reason for this difference can be shown if you darken the room. Place a tennis ball, representing the moon, where a beam of sunlight can fall upon it through a tiny chink in a curtain. Or you can use a torch as shown in Figure 18. *Can you see the ball? Does it shine by its own light or by reflected light?*

FIGURE 18. An experiment to illustrate how one half of the moon is illuminated.

Our telescopes show us much about the moon, but only about one side of it. No man has ever yet seen the other side because the moon always keeps the same side towards the earth. After you have examined as many pictures, filmstrips and slides of the moon as possible, and when you have read more about the moon, you may like to imagine what that mysterious other side is like. In a few years, perhaps, men may send a rocket round the moon and radio back to earth photographs of the hidden side.

Have you ever seen the sun and the moon in the sky at the same time ? When you see them together, they seem to be about the same size. Does it surprise you to learn that the diameter of the sun is over four hundred times the diameter of the moon ? And that the sun's volume is nearly eighty million times the volume of the moon ? Indeed the moon is much smaller than the earth, which contains enough material to make eighty-one moons. (Figure 19 shows their relative sizes.)

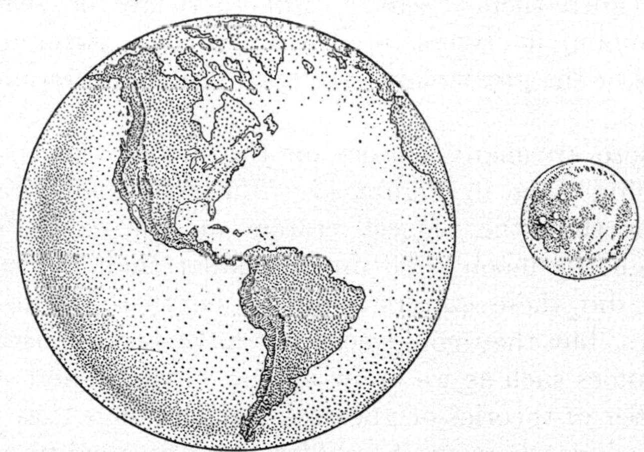

FIGURE 19. This diagram shows the relative sizes of the discs of the earth and the moon.

The sun appears to be the same size as the moon because it is about four hundred times farther away. The moon is only about 240,000 miles away from the earth. How long would such a journey take in the fastest jet aeroplane ? Of course a jet aeroplane could not go to the moon. Do you know why not ? Why do people who think of space travel plan to use rocket projectiles for transport ? Certainly the moon is so very much nearer the earth than any other neighbour in space, that the first venture in space travel is likely to be a journey to the moon.

If you could take a trip to the moon, perhaps the first thing you would notice would be the stillness, the total absence of any sound whatsoever. You know that sound usually travels through our air. There is no air on the moon. You could not hear anyone talking, or even a gunshot. Since there is no air, there is no wind. Everything is dead quiet.

There is no water there, either. Photographs show jagged peaks of rock that are never worn away by water action. Early observers saw great dark plains, and called them " seas." But there are no seas on the moon, no rivers, no lakes, no life. Around the edges of the great plains are high peaks and mountain ranges.

There are many craters on the moon. See if you can find some in Figure 17. Many of them are far bigger than the biggest craters on the earth, even though the moon is so much smaller than the earth. How did these craters come to be there ? No one knows, but they could scarcely have been caused by volcanoes such as we know on the earth. There are a number of theories or guesses. One guess is that they are regions where great bubbles of gas escaped from the molten ball before the moon cooled. If this is so, then

FIGURE 20. An artist's impression of a lunar landscape.

the craters would be like collapsed blisters, with a little volcanic material at the centre. Possibly man will never know for certain, though he will certainly go on trying to explain what he sees.

SOME THINGS YOU MAY CARE TO DO

1. Look at the moon yourself with binoculars or a small telescope. Try to find some of the dark areas shown in Figure 17. When you have focused the moon you will find that it keeps moving out of your line of sight. Why is this? Record whether it appears to move to your left or to your right.

2. If you do not own or cannot borrow binoculars or a small telescope, make one for yourself (see page 87).

3. Make a series of coloured drawings of the moon as you see it with your naked eye night by night for a month. Sometimes, of course, cloud may prevent you from seeing the moon at all; if so, record this fact carefully with the dates. With each observation and drawing record also (*a*) the time of evening when you

made the drawing, and (*b*) the direction, by magnetic compass, in which you had to look to see the moon. If you carry out these simple observations carefully you will discover several very interesting things. Also you will be teaching yourself two of the most important things in the way of a scientist—*to observe accurately* and *to record carefully.*

FIGURE 21. This photograph of the moon was taken by a schoolboy with a cheap camera and a pocket telescope.

4. Using a pocket telescope, try to take a photograph of the moon. Several tests to find the correct time exposure will be necessary. But it must be as short as possible. Why ?

5. Find a spot shaded from street lamps and house lights and point your camera at the moon. Open the shutter and leave it open for an hour's exposure. What does the developed photograph tell you about the apparent motion of the moon ? Does it show any star tracks as well ?

6. Ask your librarian to help you find pictures of landscapes of the moon which you can copy, perhaps with colours imagined by yourself, in your science notebook. Make these pictures large enough to be really attractive and do not try to crowd several on one page. Write notes of explanation under every picture.

Question 2. **Why does the Moon look different at different times of the month ?**

Just after sunset some evening you may see low in the west a very thin crescent moon. It is not visible for long, but soon sinks below the horizon. For several preceding evenings no moon at all was visible in the sky. This first thin crescent of the moon is called " the new moon." There are superstitions that you should never see it through glass, and that when you see it you should immediately turn over the money in your pocket or purse. The fact that these strange sayings are still repeated among highly-civilized people today, even if only as a joke, helps to remind us how mysterious the changing shape of the moon must be to people who know no science. Indeed in far-away parts of the world there are probably still tribes who think that each " new moon " is *really* a new moon and celebrate its birth with strange rites. Among some South American races it was once a custom, when the moon disappeared, to kill several cats as a sacrifice to the gods, to persuade them to let the moon return.

If you watch the moon night by night, after the " new " stage, you can see many interesting things, especially if you use a small telescope or binoculars. Every night the lighted portion grows bigger and bigger. Sometimes, while the lighted

FIGURE 22. " The old moon in the new moon's arms." The duller part of the moon is lit by light reflected from the earth, the brighter part by light reflected from the sun. The white spot in this photo is the planet Mars. Taken by Dr. Geo. van Biesbroesk, McDonald Observatory, April 25th, 1955. Look at Figures 21 and 27. How can you tell that this photograph was taken with a telescope ?

Courtesy Yerkes Observatory

part is still a thin crescent, you can see the rest of the moon faintly outlined by light reflected from our own earth. This is often called "the old moon in the new moon's arms."

At another stage of the growing, or *waxing* moon, you may be able to see the outline of "the man in the moon." A few days later you can see more than half of the moon, and a few days after that the glory of the "full moon."

Let us carry out an experiment to see if we can explain these changes.

PHASES OF THE MOON

Using a tennis ball and an electric torch, as shown in Figure 18, and keeping ourselves in the centre of a darkened room, let us move both the ball and the torch around us to take positions like those shown in Figure 23.

The eye shown in the middle represents our eye and we turn our eye to look directly at the tennis ball in its various positions. This is a simple experiment that you can do best in a room at home by yourself, or with one person moving the ball and torch, for you can then keep the same central position easily. If you perform the experiment carefully, you will find that when your eye is looking in the direction A, you will not see any lighted part of the tennis ball. The "new moon" stage will be found somewhere between positions A and B.

When the ball is in the position C, and your eye is turned to look directly at it, you should see one half of the surface lit up by the torch. And when the ball

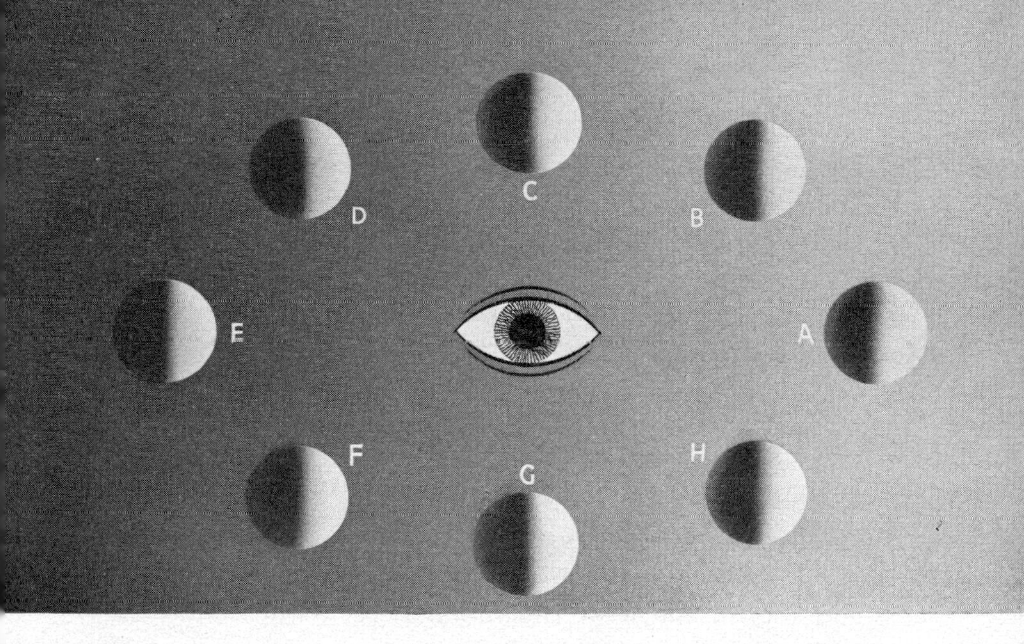

FIGURE 23.

reaches position E, then you have the position of the full moon. (Keep your head out of the way of the beam of light.)

If you carry out this experiment you will have no difficulty at all in understanding Figure 24, which shows the different " phases " of the moon. In this diagram there is, of course, the vast beam of light coming from the sun, which, you remember, has a diameter four hundred times that of the moon.

The position before the first thin streak of " new moon " is visible is sometimes called " the dark of the moon." The stage properly known as the crescent moon is roughly that given by position B. About four days later the moon is in position C. We now see one half of the lighted side ; that is, one quarter of the entire moon. This is called the *first quarter*. It is also the stage at which the moon has gone one quarter of its way round the earth.

About ten days after the dark stage the moon has reached position D and is said to be *gibbous*, which means "swelling out." Then it comes to position E about two weeks after the new moon, and from the earth we see the *full moon.* When it looks like this the moon and the earth and the sun are almost in line, the earth being between the moon and the sun as the diagram shows you. But the earth could not be *directly* in the same line with the sun and the moon or its shadow would be cast over the moon. (Why were you warned about your head in the experiment, when the tennis ball was in position E ?) However, as we shall see more clearly later, at full moon the sun and the earth and the moon are nearly in a line, and as the sun sets in the west the moon rises in the east.

A week later, the moon reaches position G. Its shape is now as it was in the first quarter. We call this phase the *last quarter*. So the moon swings round the earth, taking twenty-nine and a half days for its entire journey. Meanwhile, of course, the earth itself is on its journey round the sun, taking one year to complete this travel. But even the sun is not stationary; it is moving in the direction of the star Vega.

SOME THINGS YOU MAY CARE TO DO

1. When the moon is not full it may be either waxing or waning. Discover for yourself how to recognize immediately in which of these stages you are seeing the moon.

2. Make for yourself, in colour, a large copy of Figure 24 showing the phases of the moon.

3. Visit a museum and see if you can find there a working model to show both the earth going round the sun and the moon going round the earth.

4. The ancient Babylonians based their calendar on

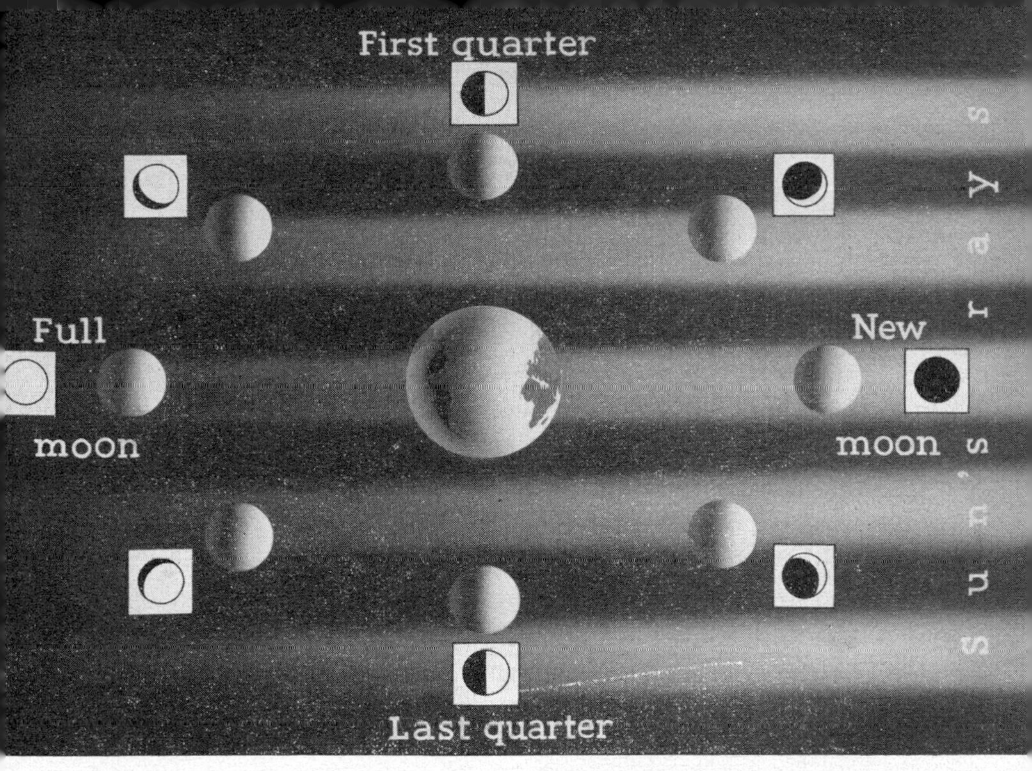

FIGURE 24. This diagram explains why the moon shows phases to inhabitants of the earth. Remember that the beams of light from the sun do not in fact have dark spaces between them. But the artist has shown the sunlight in this way in order to make the diagram tell its story more clearly.

the regular return of the new moon, that is on the first thin crescent which can be seen in the west after sunset. See if you can find anything more about the calendar of the Babylonians, and about the Jewish calendar. The Babylonians thought that the 7th, 14th, 21st and 28th days of every moon were unlucky days, and it was forbidden that certain people should then do certain things. Can you see how this may have helped to make a seven-day week ? And can you see a possible origin of the word *month* ?

5. With the help of your librarian prepare a group report on the ways in which Red Indians, Mexicans, Incas, and other ancient peoples of the Americas fixed their calendar by using the movements of the moon.

Question 3. **Does the Moon really influence our lives ?**

Untrue beliefs. Have you ever heard that if you sleep in the light of the full moon you will become a lunatic ? Many people used to believe this very foolish idea ; in fact, the very word " lunatic " comes from *luna*, the Latin word for *moon*. You are probably familiar with the old word " moon-struck " which has the same idea.

There are other superstitions about the moon that some people believe, even today. How silly it is to think that it really makes any difference whether you see the new moon over your left or over your right shoulder ! Some people think that it makes a difference whether you sow your seeds at a time of full moon or " in the dark of the moon." But scientists, despite experiments, have been unable to find any truth in this. Nor have scientists been able to find any evidence at all for theories that the moon affects the weather. So when you hear people say such things as " We shall have a change in the weather with the new moon," you should remember that scientists regard this as mere superstition. But it would be best if you would carefully record these statements when you hear them and check them up, with dates and times, for yourself. Then you will see how much truth there may be in them. There is, however, one weather sign connected with the moon which may give information to weather-men (or *meteorologists* as they are called). This is the coloured ring or *halo* which can occasionally be seen round the moon. It is caused by light reflected from tiny ice crystals very high in the air and so it can give some information which may be used in forecasting the weather.

In the ways mentioned so far the moon has no influence on our lives. But there is at least one way in which it has important effects, for it causes the tides in the oceans and seas of the world. Even if your only interest in the sea is bathing, you must usually pay attention to the tide. If you are staying near a sandy beach, you may prefer to bathe when the tide is well out, so that you may have the wide beach to play on. On the other hand, if you bathe off the rocks, high tide may give you better conditions.

Naturally, people had observed the effects of the tides for centuries, but no one was able to give any satisfactory scientific explanation until Sir Isaac Newton proposed the theory of *gravitation*. According to this theory, every particle of matter in the entire universe is constantly attracting every other particle. For example, every particle of matter on the earth is attracted by the moon, and also by the sun. The solid parts of the earth are not free to move, but water, being liquid, actually moves in the direction of the attraction. It heaps up like a big wave. Since

FIGURE 25. High tides on the earth follow the moon.

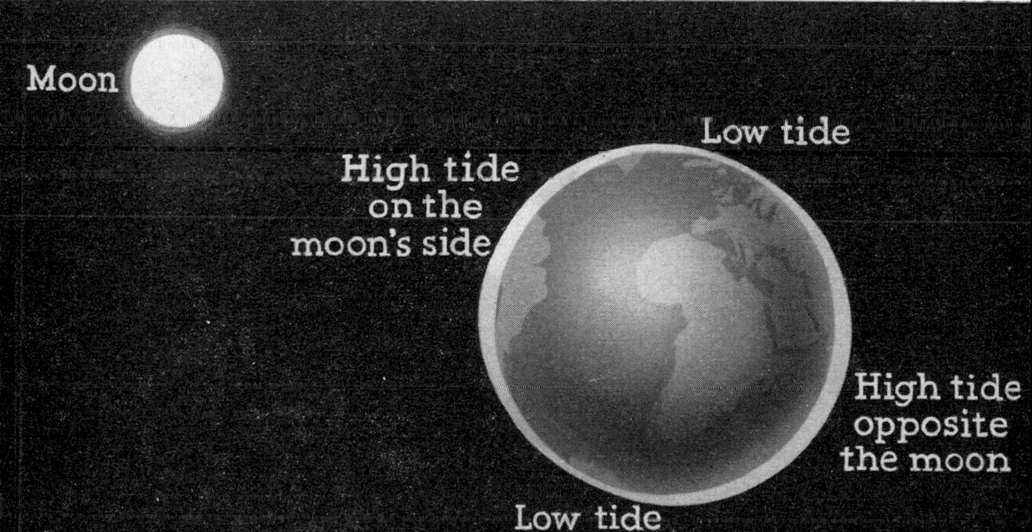

the sun is so much larger than the moon, you might expect its pull to be greater, but the moon is so much nearer the earth that it has a greater effect upon the tides.

The course of the daily tides on the earth goes like this. There is a gradual rise of water on the shore for just over six hours, and then the tide gradually goes out during another period of just over six hours. The highest stage is known as *high tide* and the lowest as *low tide*.

But if you have lived by the sea, or stayed by the sea for several weeks on end, you will know that at certain times of the month the tide is greater than at other times. On some days each month the tide comes in higher at high tide and goes out farther at low tide than on other days in the month. To understand why, you must remember that both the moon and the sun are pulling the earth's water, thus producing both *lunar tides* and *solar tides*.

When the sun and the moon are pulling in the same direction, as shown in Figure 26, the solar and the lunar tides reinforce each other and we have the extra high tides known as *spring tides*. Why are the spring tides at the same time as new moon and full moon ? Note that spring tides have nothing to do with the season of spring, for spring tides occur twice a month ! The word comes from Anglo-Saxon and means *springing* or *leaping* tides.

FIGURE 26. *Spring* tides occur every two weeks when the moon's pull is in the same line as the sun's pull.

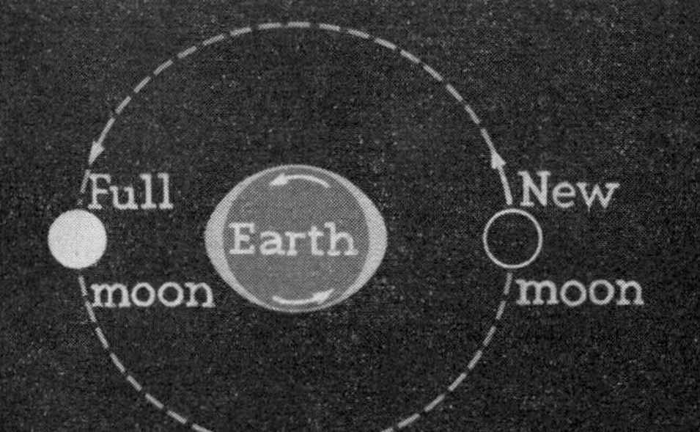

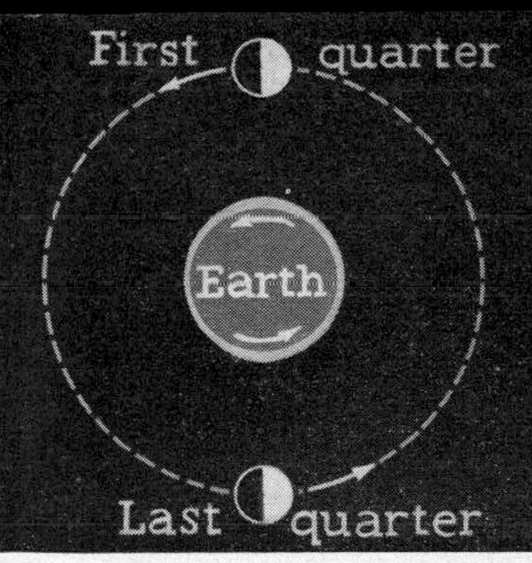

FIGURE 27. *Neap* tides occur every two weeks when the moon's pull is at right angles to the sun's pull.

But, twice a month, the moon and the sun are pulling in directions which are at right angles to each other (see Figure 27). Then the solar and lunar tides weaken each other and the high tides are not so high and the low tides are not so low. These tides are called *neap tides* from an Anglo-Saxon word which means *scanty*.

If you do not find it easy to understand why the pulls of the sun and moon are sometimes at right angles to each other look ahead to Figure 29.

Tidal variation. You may now think that tides ebb and flow in exactly the same way all over the world, but this is not so. The movement of the water round the earth is blocked here and there, sometimes by the great masses of land, and sometimes by small islands or capes. So the water goes round on both sides but takes different times by the different routes. Thus there are a few places that have four tides a day and some that have only one. The general pattern, however, is that there is an average period of about twelve hours and twenty-five minutes between one high tide and the next, so that most coastal places get two tides in just over a day.

But the Mediterranean Sea is practically tideless—the difference between high and low tides being only a matter of some six inches. The reason, of course, is that the narrow Straits of Gibraltar make the Mediterranean almost into a landlocked sea. When we examine seas which are completely inland ones, like the Caspian, the tidal effect is too small to be noticed.

Tides are valuable to man in a number of ways. They keep the waters of bays and harbours in motion, thus clearing out rubbish which might collect and make unhealthy conditions. And low tides enable men to gather kinds of food which they would not otherwise find it easy to get—oysters, winkles, cockles, mussels, shrimps, clams and kinds of edible seaweed.

At high tides vessels can enter harbours and docks which are well inland and which could not be reached if the water were always at the same level. The Port of London is just such a case: without the tides there would be no docks near to London Bridge.

SOME THINGS YOU MAY CARE TO DO

1. See if you can obtain, from at least two different seaside places not very near to one another, calendars that show the times of high and low tide. Try to account for the difference in time. (Ask the librarian to show you a *Nautical Almanac.*)

2. With the aid of a diagram work out for yourself why it is that the high tides at most places are every day about fifty minutes later than they were the previous day. (Hint: remember that it takes the moon 29½ days to go completely round the earth. For a rough calculation we can call this 30 days. This means that to get to the same position with regard to any place on the earth's surface, after the earth has done one day's journey, the moon must take one day and an extra thirtieth of a day. Perhaps you can now finish the sum and draw a diagram.)

3. In some river mouths, at certain seasons, the high tides cause the river water to roll upstream like a tidal wave. In England there is the Severn " bore " and the Trent " eagre." See if your librarian can help you to find information and pictures of such things. If so, copy a picture into your science notebook.

Problem B : How important is the Moon ?

Question 4. **What part does the Moon play in Eclipses ?**

Anyone who has had the good fortune to see a total eclipse of the sun will admit that it is a very remarkable, and an awe-inspiring, experience. Not only does the daylight dim as a dark body creeps over the face of the sun, but one feels everything around growing cooler and silent. For the birds cease to twitter and the grasshoppers cease to chirrup ; even the flies cease to buzz. It is no wonder that for thousands of years unlearned people thought that eclipses of the sun foretold terrible happenings like plagues and floods.

But for thousands of years, in different parts of the world, there have also been scientists who, though they had no idea of the cause of plagues, knew how eclipses of the sun happen and could even predict the actual day many years before the event would happen. But without printing, or schools for everyone, it was not possible to share this knowledge very widely. So to most people eclipses of the sun remained a frightening mystery. There are also eclipses of the moon and they, too, were often taken as evil omens. The word eclipse comes from an ancient Greek word meaning *a failing.* In eclipse of sun or moon the light fails.

About four hundred years ago a young Danish boy, the son of a nobleman, saw a total eclipse of the sun and was so stirred that he later became an astronomer, in spite of the opposition of all his relatives. This was a

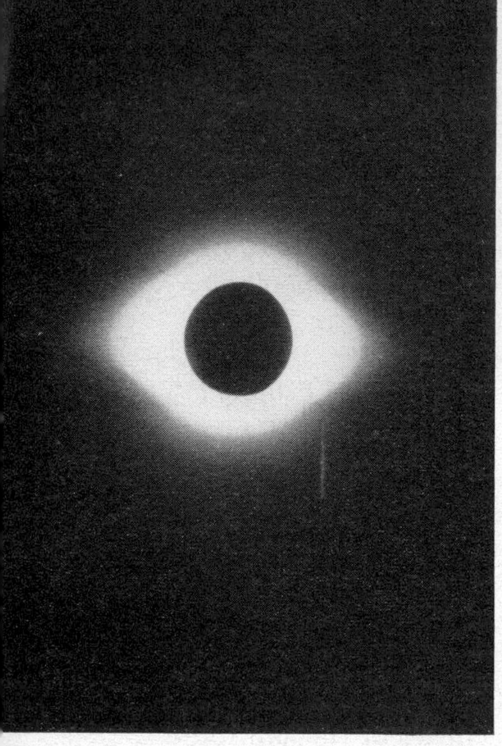

Central Press Photos, Ltd.

FIGURE 28. This photograph of the total eclipse of June 30th, 1954 (see Figure 1), was taken from an aeroplane with the Astronomer Royal on board. It flew high over the North Atlantic in the path of the Total Eclipse. Was 1954 a year of sun-spot maximum ?

very good thing for us, for he invented the most accurate instruments for measuring the movements of the planets that had ever been known, except perhaps in China, and his work provided some of the clues that led to Sir Isaac Newton's law of gravitation a hundred years later.

And we have already learned that eclipses of the sun are still events of great importance to scientists. Look at Figure 28. What is the black disc in the centre of the picture ? If this really is the moon why does it only occasionally come into this position as it moves round the earth ?

To answer this question we must look first at Figure 29. We notice that the path which the moon traces round the moving earth is at an angle with the path that the earth follows on its year-long journey round the sun. Actually, the angle is far less than that shown in our diagram, which cannot be drawn to scale on the page of our book without making the moon almost too small to be seen. But the effect of this slope of the moon's path to the earth's path is that the moon does not pass directly between the sun and the earth every time it goes round the earth.

FIGURE 29. This diagram, which is NOT drawn to scale, should help you to see why eclipses of the sun are not very frequent. Why is the diagram not drawn to scale ? See the table on page 64.

Instead it passes across the sun's face, as seen from the earth, not more than five times a year and not less than twice a year. The variable number of times is due to regular disturbances of the moon's movement which are caused by the pull of the sun upon it. If it were not for the sun and the planets the moon's path round the earth would be a perfect ellipse. But can we think of the earth without the sun ?

If we look back at the diagram of the phases of the moon we see that when the moon comes directly between the earth and the sun this must be exactly at the time of the new moon. On these occasions the shadow of the moon traces a path on part of the earth as shown by AB in Figure 30. This path is only

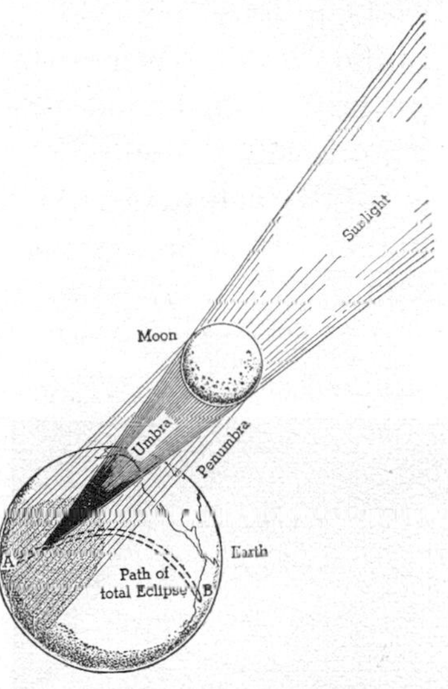

FIGURE 30. An eclipse of the sun. The cone of the moon's umbra traces the path of total eclipse.

about a hundred miles wide. Within this path an eclipse is total. You are fortunate if you ever see a total eclipse of the sun, because *at any given place* on the earth a total eclipse is visible only about three times in a thousand years.

Outside the path traced out by the dark shadow called the *umbra* (Latin for *shade*), in the area covered by the *penumbra* (*almost shade*), the eclipse when seen is only *partial*, that is only a part of the sun's disc is obscured by the moon.

Eclipses of the Moon. Just as the moon may be in a straight line with the sun and the earth and between them, and thus eclipse the sun, so the earth can eclipse the moon. If you look at Figures 24 and 29 you will see that this can only happen when the moon is full and when the angle between its path and the earth's path puts it exactly into the right position. The earth casts a long pointed shadow behind it for nearly a million miles. When the moon moves into this shadow, its face is darkened, for no sunlight falls upon it (see Figure 32). You may be surprised, when the moon is totally eclipsed, that its face does not become wholly black. This is because the earth's atmosphere bends some of the sun's rays so that a little light falls upon the moon after all. These give the moon a lurid coppery red hue ; we cannot be surprised that ignorant people used to consider eclipses, even of the moon, as evil omens !

FIGURE 31. Photo of a partial eclipse of the moon.

Courtesy Royal Greenwich Observatory

1. Demonstrate eclipses of the moon and sun. For this demonstration the room should be darkened if possible ; a small geographical globe or a fairly large ball represents the earth ; and a small white ball represents the moon. Hold the moon about six inches away from the earth, and move it to represent the motion of the moon on its path ; in one position the light of the sun does not reach the moon. The earth is then between the sun and the moon, and the moon is eclipsed.

FIGURE 32. A demonstration with an electric bulb, a globe and tennis balls to show an eclipse of the moon.

Now rearrange the moon so that a shadow of it is cast upon the earth. To a person standing in that shadow the sun would be eclipsed. If you now spin the globe that represents the earth you will be able to get an eclipse track like that shown in Figure 30.

2. Turn up the word " eclipse " in the index to the current edition of *Whitaker's Almanack* and find details of the eclipses of sun and moon due to take place during the year. Then consider whether there will be any chance of your seeing any of these eclipses.

3. By turning through the copies of *Whitaker's Almanack* for the last five years draw up a report for your class on the eclipses that have taken place in this period. This report is best prepared by a group of pupils, each taking one year. If you want pictures of these eclipses you can usually find them, a few days after the event, in *The Illustrated London News* or *The Sphere.* Many libraries keep back copies of these magazines. If the librarian lets you use these back numbers, take some coloured crayons with you and make coloured copies of pictures direct into your science notebook. Do not forget to give the date of the issue from which you make your notes and copy the pictures.

4. Prepare a talk for your class on astronomy in China before the birth of Christ. In *History of Astronomy* by G. Abetti (published by Sidgwick and Jackson) you can read of two astronomers, Ho and Hi, who were put to death before 2000 B.C. because an eclipse took place which they had failed to predict. Your librarian will probably aid you to find help from other books and encyclopedias.

5. Read in the Bible two passages which probably refer to eclipses. These are Joel, Chapter ii, verse 31, and Amos, Chapter viii, verse 9. The latter is thought to refer to the eclipse of the sun which took place on June 15th in the year 763 B.C. What comments would you make about the verse from Joel ?

6. The name of the Danish astronomer mentioned on page 45 was Tycho Brahe. The story of his life is fascinating. Read about him in a large encyclopedia and so prepare a talk for your class. If you are very lucky you may find in your public library a copy of one of the very few books written in English about this fine scientist, who was very much " a character."

Problem C: **WHAT IS THE SOLAR SYSTEM?**

Before 1543 nobody thought of the sun having a family, or satellites, as we call them in astronomy. Everyone till then, with the exception of a few ancient Greeks, was certain that the earth was the centre of the universe and that the sun moved round the earth every day. Does the moon move round the earth and is it a satellite of the earth?

Suddenly in 1543 a book by the 70-year-old Polish priest and scientist, Nicholas Kopernik, who had spent much of his life recording the nightly paths of the planets, declared that the stars and the planets did *not* go round the earth, but that the earth and the other planets were all of them going round the sun, each of them in its own circle.

Mansell Collection

FIGURE 33. Nicholas Kopernik, 1473–1543: " The man who put the earth in its place."

This amazing discovery was *almost* right. Perhaps you know what was the error? If Kopernik (or Copernicus) had had a telescope and more accurate instruments, he might have got his explanation absolutely right.

Do you think it required any courage to be *the only man in the world* to hold that theory? Perhaps you know what happened to Galileo some years later for believing in the theory of Copernicus? In this connection you may remember how, in Unit 1, when we talked of " The way of a Scientist," we said " *A scientist believes that it is his business to find the truth without minding whether people make fun of him or praise him.*"

Question 1. **What is the difference between Stars and Planets ?**

Ever since the time of the earliest men the night sky must have been a thing of wonder. In some of the dry regions of the world such as Persia and Arabia and Egypt, where the sky is clear on most nights, and in many parts of China too, early scientists thousands of years ago noticed that some stars were different from others. These " stars " shone with a steadier, less twinkling, light. More important still, they did not keep their place in the mighty procession that appears to sweep across the sky every night. When a great procession marches through a city, like the annual Lord Mayor's procession in London, every group must keep its proper distance from the ones in front and behind. But a few police on horseback go up and down the sides, and these may be compared with the " stars " that do not keep their position in the great march past. The ancient scientists called these " unfixed " stars *wanderers* and their word for a wanderer was *planet*.

All the other stars, which these early astronomers called " fixed " stars, were divided up into groups of stars. Each group was named after some animal, person or thing suggested by the outline of the stars in the group. These groups of stars have the long name *constellation* which is a word made up from Latin words which mean *a group of stars*. But it is convenient to have this word to mean a special group of stars such as the Great Bear, the Little Bear, Orion the Hunter, Pegasus the Winged Horse, and Andromeda the beautiful but unfortunate princess who was chained to a rock, according to the old Greek stories.

The ancient astronomers of Babylon, Persia, Egypt

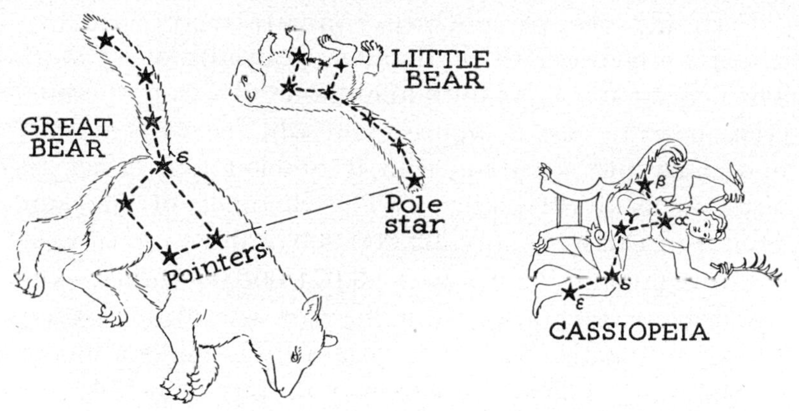

From Beet: "A Guide to the Sky," by permission of the University Press, Cambridge

FIGURE 34. Three of the chief constellations in the sky of the northern hemisphere.

and Greece knew and named five planets—Mercury, Venus, Mars, Jupiter and Saturn. Since the invention of the telescope, astronomers have found more—Uranus, Neptune and Pluto. Pluto was discovered only as recently as 1930.

Telescopes have shown us a big difference between planets and stars. In the telescope a planet appears as a circular disc, but even a photograph of a star shows it with, as it were, points of light; in fact "star-shaped" as we say. Partly this is because the planets only reflect the light of the sun, while stars give out their own light, and partly this is the result of the unimaginable distances that the light from the stars has come. American astronomers searching the sky with the wonderful telescope on Mount Palomar in California have photographed stars which are so far away that the light has taken 500 million years to reach the telescope from the star! Yet light travels at 186,000 miles a second!

But the planets are comparatively near and the light from the farthest of them reaches us in a few hours.

Certainly the planets are comparatively near the sun if we consider their distance from any other star. The nearest star is six million million miles from the sun. (If you write this in figures you will see why mathematicians and scientists find it quicker and easier to write it as 6.10^{12} miles.) The distance of the sun from the earth is only 93,000,000 miles and though Pluto is much farther away—3,671,000,000 miles—yet the nearest star, other than the sun, is still more than 1600 times farther away. If you were to make a model of the sun's family in which you put a pebble for Pluto five yards away from a football standing for the sun, in what town or village near your home would you have to put a football for the nearest star? [Hint: for a rough answer use 1760 instead of 1600.]

Though it is partly because the planets are so near to our own star, the sun, that they are called "the sun's family" or solar system, there are other reasons too. Firstly they all move round the sun and follow it on its journey through space. Also they all move round the sun in the same direction, they all spin as they move, and they all spin in the same direction, and this direction is the same as that in which the sun spins. As a result many astronomers have thought that the planets must, in some way or other, have originated from the sun. They may not be right, and perhaps men

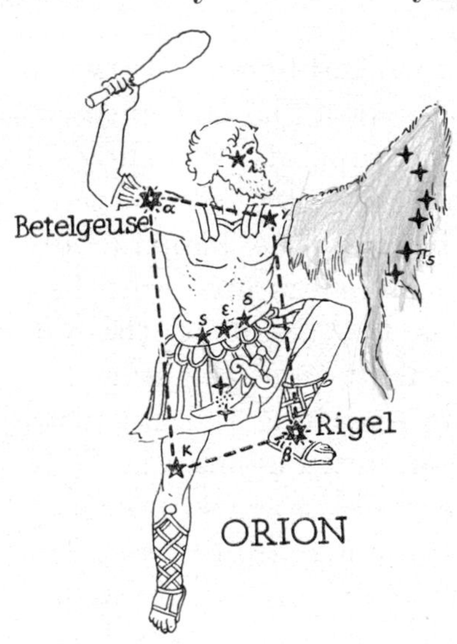

From Beet: "A Guide to the Sky," by permission of the University Press, Cambridge

FIGURE 35. The constellation of Orion the Hunter.

may never have any way of being certain, but at present it still seems at least a possibility.

As you can imagine, the mass of the sun is enormously greater than that of all the planets put together. So the planets are kept from straying away from the sun by that strange pull which all objects have for all other objects. We call this the *force of gravity* when it pulls an apple to the earth, or the *force of gravitation* when it pulls one heavenly body to another.

It was by mathematics that Isaac Newton established the law of gravitation. But he could not have done this had it not been for the previous mathematical work of a German astronomer called John Kepler. Kopernik had thought that the planets go round the sun in *circles*. Kepler showed that they actually go round in *ellipses*, with the sun at one of the focal points. But the ellipses are very nearly circles and it was the measurements, not the mathematics, of Kopernik that were at fault.

SOME THINGS YOU MAY CARE TO DO

1. Make some neat drawings of ellipses, some of them elongated and some of them nearly circular. To do this, take a length of string fixed at each end as at F_1 and F_2 in the diagram, and move a pencil so that it is just held by the string. Each point F is a focus of the ellipse. Move the foci nearer and nearer together and compare the shape of the ellipses that you draw. When does the ellipse become a circle ?

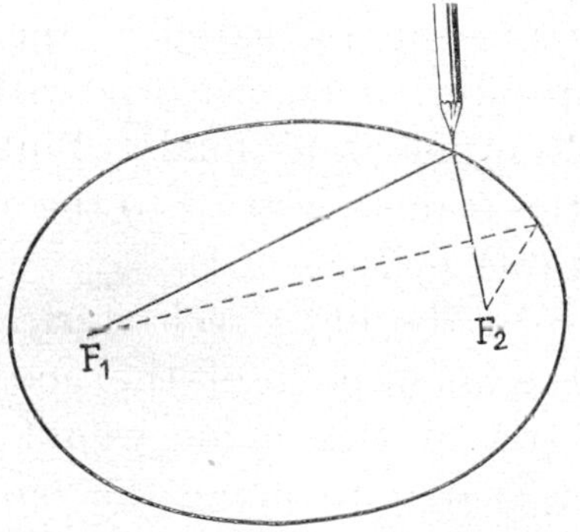

FIGURE 36. How to draw an ellipse. F_1 and F_2 are the two focal points or *foci*. What is the singular of foci ?

2. Look at the sky on clear nights and do not rest content until you can pick out the following constellations: (*a*) if you live in the northern hemisphere—the Great Bear, the Little Bear, Perseus, Cassiopeia, Andromeda, and some of the seasonal constellations like Orion the Hunter; (*b*) if you live in the southern hemisphere—the Southern Cross, the Peacock, the Toucan, the Phoenix, the Keel of the Ship, the Greater and Lesser Magellanic Clouds, the Crane, and the same seasonal constellations as for the northern hemisphere.

Why do both hemispheres see the same *seasonal* stars?

3. Perhaps small groups of the class can prepare talks on the lives of the following scientists, each of whom helped to prepare the way for the work of the next: Kopernik, Tycho Brahe, Kepler, Galileo, Isaac Newton, William Herschel and his sister Caroline.

Problem C: **What is the Solar System?**

Question 2. **What do we know about some of the Planets?**

Look back to Figure 2. In the centre is the sun. The innermost planet is Mercury. Next comes Venus. Then the earth, with a small white dot near it to represent its satellite the moon. Then Mars, then Jupiter, then Saturn with its rings, then Uranus, Neptune, and finally Pluto. As you would expect, the planets nearest to the sun go round fastest (see the table on page 64).

In the old Greek stories Mercury was the name of the messenger of the gods. So the Greek scientists thought this name would also suit the planet which appeared to move the most swiftly among the fixed stars. But in northern latitudes it is not easily seen, for it is usually low on the horizon and disappears soon after sunset.

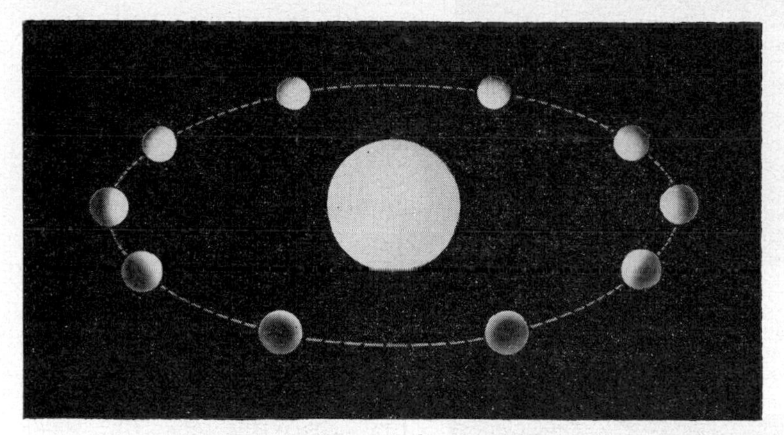

FIGURE 37. This diagram illustrates why Venus shows phases to an observer on the earth.

Venus is the other planet which is nearer to the sun than is the earth. There is no difficulty in seeing Venus, for it is often the brightest object in the sky and is more than twice as big as Mercury. At part of its course round the sun it is a brilliant " star " in the evening sky before the true stars have appeared. At another stage it is a morning star hardly blotted out by sunrise. At times it can be seen even at mid-day and people who did not know anything about astronomy have been alarmed by the sight. Until the year 1610 even men who had studied the sky had been unable to explain why Venus went through a cycle of being brighter and then less bright and so on.

But when Galileo studied it through his telescope he discovered that the variation in its brightness was due to " phases " just like those of the moon (see page 36). Sometimes Galileo could see the full face of Venus, sometimes he could see half of it and sometimes only a crescent, or none at all. Look at Figure 37 and work out for yourself the positions when Venus

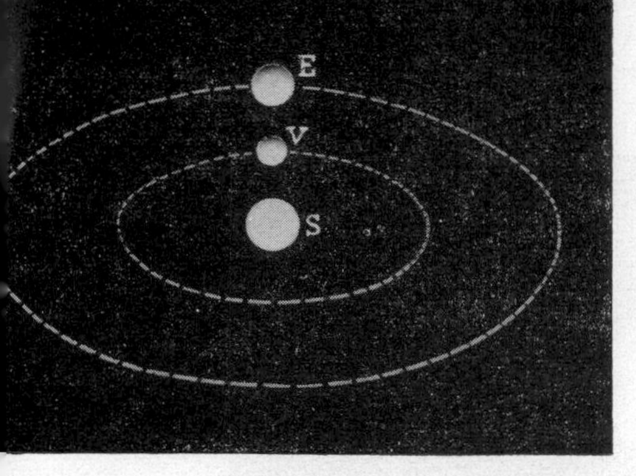

FIGURE 38.

(*a*) Here the earth, Venus and the sun are shown in the same line. Mercury is not included in these diagrams.

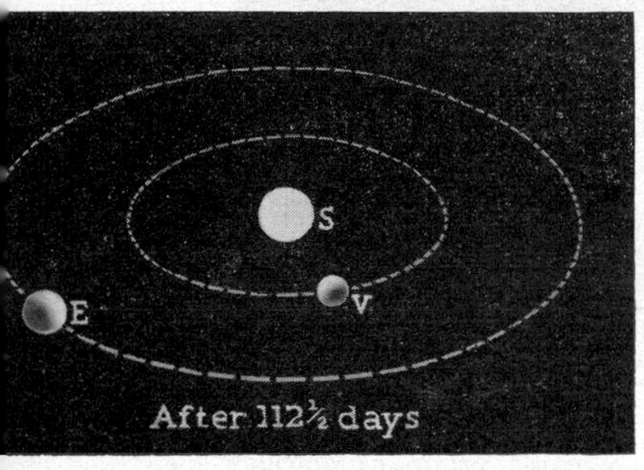

(*b*) The earth has moved about a third of its way round the sun. How long does this take ? Venus has moved more than half its way round the sun.

(*c*) 225 days have passed and Venus is back into the same *relative* position as in (*a*). The earth has gone less than two-thirds of its way round the sun. Meanwhile the sun itself has been moving in the direction of the star Vega.

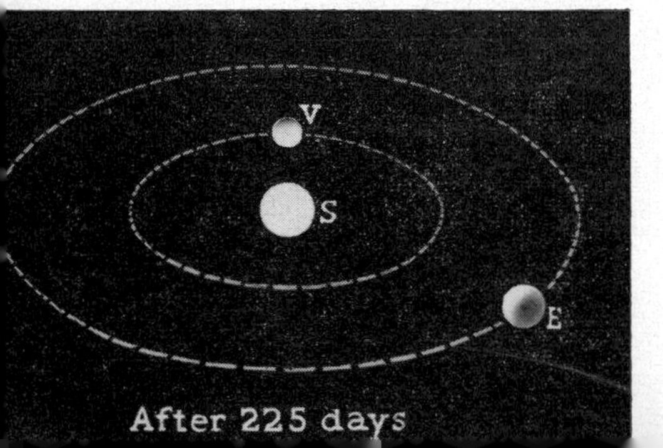

would be seen full face. When would it not be seen at all by someone in the direction marked " Observer " ?

Figure 37 would be inaccurate if we supposed that the " observer " represents the position of someone on the earth for all the 225 days that Venus takes to go round the sun. Can you see why ? Try drawing *six* or *seven* diagrams to show the positions of Venus and the earth at intervals of $112\frac{1}{2}$ days, which is half the time that Venus takes to go round the sun. To start with, take the position when the sun, Venus and the earth are all in the same straight line in your diagram and Venus is between the earth and the sun. Do your diagrams explain why Venus *actually appears bigger* at some times than at other times ?

Look at Venus on most nights for a few months and see if you can notice any difference in brightness over this period of time. What standard of brightness could you use to make your comparison and to keep your record ?

Mars

This is the planet which is most like the earth. Its mass, however, is one-ninth of that of the earth and its gravity less than two-fifths of that of the earth. So a person weighing 150 pounds on the earth would weigh less than 60 pounds on Mars!

But the most important points about Mars are that it has an atmosphere (though there is very little oxygen in it); around the poles there are ice-caps (though they are very thin); there are greenish and brownish areas which undergo seasonal change. Mid-day temperatures in the tropics of Mars would suit a human being, though the nights are very cold. All these things make it possible that living things of some kind *may* exist on Mars, though the climate and atmosphere of Mars would kill most kinds of plants known on our earth. Mars got its name—that of the god of War—because of the reddish tinge it generally shows. Scientists have evidence that the reddish and yellowish expanses that cover about three-quarters of the surface of Mars are covered with dust and sand; they are bone-dry Martian deserts.

FIGURE 39. Mars photographed in blue and red light by the 200-inch Hale telescope at Mount Palomar.

Courtesy Mount Wilson & Palomar Observatories

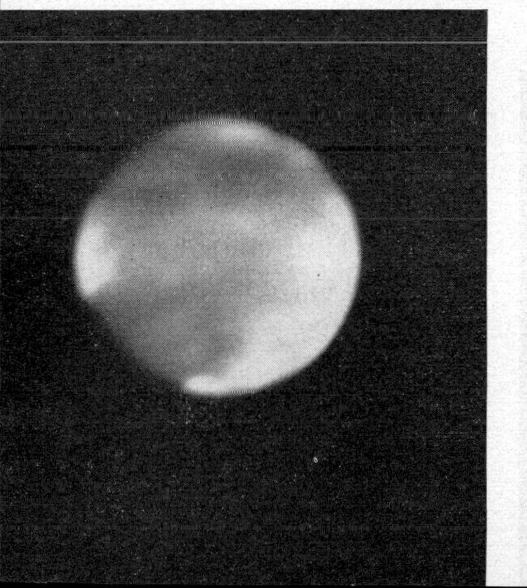

Jupiter

This is by far the largest of all the planets and could easily contain all the others. Yet despite its huge bulk Jupiter spins in less than 10 hours! Astronomers feel certain that the surface which they see is not solid and one of them thinks that the central rocky core of Jupiter is only 37,000 miles across and that around this is a belt 17,000 miles thick of solidified gases. Perhaps this belt is like some of our own highest clouds which consist of ice crystals. Then around this there may be an atmosphere 8000 miles deep. How thick do we consider the atmosphere of the earth to be?

In the sky Jupiter is an outstandingly bright object though Venus is more brilliant and so is Mars from time to time. With even a small telescope or very good binoculars we can see that the disc of Jupiter is somewhat flattened at the poles and that the surface appears to be divided into belts. We can also see the four bright moons which were discovered by Galileo in 1610. With bigger telescopes astronomers see a continual movement in the belts. This movement is so rapid that they talk of Jupiter's *turmoil* or *turbulence*. Telescopes of moderate or large size are required to see the colour changes, which include brown, red, pink, orange, yellow, green, blue and purple. For more than sixty years observers of the Jupiter section of the British Astronomical Association, most of whom are amateurs, have been watching and recording

FIGURE 40. Jupiter, in blue light, showing the Great Red Spot. Above Jupiter you can see the white spot of the satellite Ganymede and the dark spot of its shadow appears above the Great Red Spot. This photograph was taken by the 200-inch Hale telescope on Mount Palomar.

Courtesy Mount Wilson & Palomar Observatories

every change that can be seen in Jupiter's atmosphere. Perhaps one day you will make your own telescope and become a member of such a group? Quite a number of schools have their own telescope, often made by the school astronomical group. (See Figure 43.)

Saturn

Everyone knows of Saturn's rings. Not everyone knows that sometimes they are seen as wide belts extending beyond the planet for a distance more than half its diameter, and that sometimes they appear as a thin line running across the face of the planet.

Look at Figure 41, which shows not only the different rings, but also why they appear differently to us on the earth at periods which may be a long time apart, for this planet takes 29½ years to travel round the sun.

Saturn is the second largest planet, with a diameter

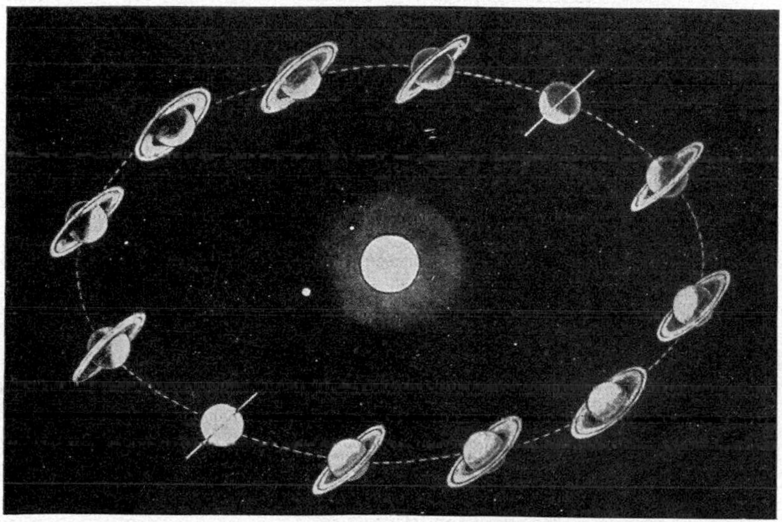

From Davidson: "From Atoms to Stars," by permission of Hutchinson & Co. (Publishers), Ltd.

Figure 41. This diagram is NOT drawn to scale. The small spot is the earth. You can see that in the course of the years we get very different views of Saturn's rings.

Courtesy Mount Wilson & Palomar Observatories

FIGURE 42. Saturn and its system of rings, photographed by the 100-inch telescope on Mount Wilson.

of 75,100 miles at the equator, but of only 67,200 miles from pole to pole. How do these measurements compare with those of the earth ?

The rings have a diameter of nearly 170,000 miles, but they are exceedingly thin—perhaps less than ten miles in thickness. For hundreds of years astronomers have wondered what these rings could be made of. The latest idea is that they consist of small pieces of rock, perhaps no bigger than pebbles, together with coarse sand made by the pebbles when they collide. Perhaps there will be quite a different theory one day : there have certainly been lots of theories to try to explain the divisions between the rings.

But there are certain interesting things that scientists *know* about Saturn. We know, for instance, that it is made of material so light that it would float in water. Some of the things we know about Saturn have a lucky connection with 9½ that helps our memories ; thus Saturn's diameter is roughly 9½ times that of the earth, it is 9½ times as far from the sun, its mass is 95 times that of the earth and its " year " is 29½ of our years.

URANUS

This planet was not known to ancient astronomers, for it is almost invisible to the naked eye, though it can just be seen on a very clear dark night. But more than 150 years passed after the invention of the telescope before the planet was found, by accident, by the astronomer Sir William Herschel. You will find some facts about it in the table on page 64.

Uranus has five satellites, with the fairy names of Ariel, Umbriel, Titania, Oberon and Miranda. Have you met any of these names anywhere else ?

Neptune

The existence of this planet was predicted by two brilliant young mathematicians who were seeking an explanation for the slight irregular movement of Uranus. You can read the quite exciting story in Davidson's *Astronomy for Everyman*.

Neptune has two satellites, named Triton and Nereid. Do you think that these names are very suitable ? [Hint : look up the names in a book of reference.]

Pluto

Pluto was discovered in somewhat the same way as Neptune. First its existence was predicted to explain the irregular movements of Uranus, which had not been completely cleared up, and then the part of the sky where it might be was carefully photographed. Only after months of painstaking study of the photographs was the planet found. This was in 1930.

It was not until 1950 that astronomers, using the enormous 200 inch telescope, were able to get an accurate measurement of Pluto's diameter—it was 3700 miles. How does this compare with the diameter of the earth ?

There is still a good deal that astronomers want to know about Pluto, including how a planet of this size can have the pull on Uranus and Neptune which was calculated unless it is much denser than the earth. Compare the densities of the other planets in the table below and you will see why this is such an interesting point.

SOME FACTS ABOUT THE PLANETS

Name	Mean distance from the sun in millions of miles	Time of revolution round the sun	Equatorial Diameter (approx.) in miles	Density (Water = 1)
MERCURY	36	88 days	3100	3·8
VENUS .	67	226 ,,	7700	4·9
EARTH .	93	365¼ ,,	7900	5·5
MARS .	142	687 ,,	4200	4·0
JUPITER .	483	12 years approx.	89,000	1·3
SATURN .	886	30 ,, ,,	75,000	0·7
URANUS .	1782	84 ,, ,,	32,000	1·3
NEPTUNE	2792	165 ,, ,,	28,000	2·2
PLUTO .	3671	248 ,, ,,	3700	?

THE SUN AND MOON

Name	Approx. mean distance from earth	Time of revolution round the earth	Diameter (approx.) in miles	Density (Water = 1)
SUN . .	93,000,000	—	866,000	1·4
MOON .	240,000	29½ days	2000	3·4

FIGURE 43. A school observatory constructed by the Physics Master and boys at King Edward VI Grammar School, Stratford-on-Avon.

Courtesy D. G. A. Dyson

SOME THINGS YOU MAY CARE TO DO

1. Taking an orange to represent Jupiter, make models on the right scale to represent the other planets and mount them on corks with needles, or on small blocks of wood, so that you can move them about. Then, using Mercury as the starting point and putting Venus 3 inches away, place all the other models at a proper scale distance. How far from Mercury should you put a model of the sun and what would be the diameter of this model ?

2. By using *Whitaker's Almanack* or *The Times* book of the stars month by month called *The Night Sky*, find which planets are visible in the northern hemisphere and use the maps in the book to help you find them. *Whitaker's Almanack* will also give you a good deal of up-to-date general information about the planets.

3. If Jupiter is visible at a suitable time, try to see its satellites by using a small telescope. If Saturn is visible look for its rings.

4. If you live near London make a visit to the Science Museum at South Kensington where you will find many interesting models of the solar system, some of which may be made to work by turning a handle.

Problem C : **What is the Solar System ?**

Question 3. **What other members of the Solar System are there ?**

The planets are not the only satellites of the sun. Between the paths of Mars and Jupiter there move several thousand small bodies known as planetoids. Several of these can be compared in size with the moon (see Figure 44), but the majority are very much smaller than the named ones shown. Many of them are only a mile or two in diameter. When newly-discovered planetoids are big enough they are given

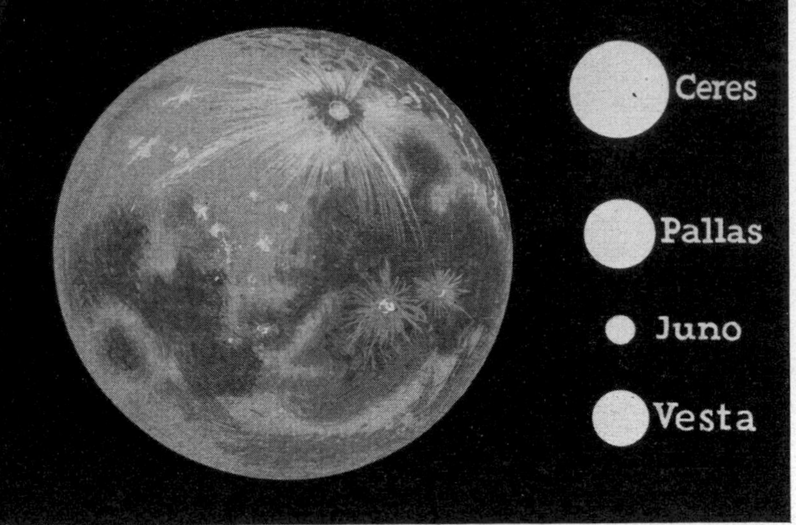

FIGURE 44. This diagram shows the size of four of the minor planets compared with the moon.

a feminine name ; if, besides size, there is something interesting about them, they are given a masculine name !

Now that we have radio telescopes, such as the huge one at Jodrell Bank, Manchester (see Frontispiece), we are likely to learn a lot more about planetoids. For though such tiny celestial bodies are very difficult to find with an *optical* telescope, they readily reflect back radio waves when these are directed into the sky.

COMETS

Most people have read about comets because of their long glowing tails and because the appearance of a comet in the sky used to be taken as a sign of evil about to come. For instance, it is said that the appearance of Halley's comet in A.D. 66 was interpreted as a warning to the Jews that Jerusalem would shortly be destroyed. When the same comet was seen in England in 1066 it was a sign that England would be conquered by the Normans. But it also frightened some of the men of William of Normandy and it is depicted in the Bayeux tapestry.

Associated Press, Ltd.

FIGURE 45. This comet, which appeared in 1957, shows the long tail pointing away from the sun, and also a well-developed " beard " pointing towards the sun. The cone of the comet has a diameter of about 40,000 miles (compare this with the diameter of the earth). Its tail is at least 15 million miles long. Photographed by Dr. R. L. Waterfield on April 22nd, 1957, at Ascot, Surrey, with 8 minutes exposure.

But the interesting long tail is not the most important part of a comet. The tail only develops as the comet comes near to the sun and the rays of the sun drive tiny particles of matter (less than 0·00004 of an inch in diameter) from the head of the comet into the gases streaming behind it. Because of the pressure of the sun's rays upon these particles the tail always points *away* from the sun.

The head of a comet consists of fragments of matter of all sizes from specks of dust to solid lumps as big as a house. This assortment of material is spread out over a volume which may be half as great as that of the earth. There are about one hundred known comets and they vary greatly in size and in path. Most of them, like some planetoids, have long elliptical paths the planes of which cross the plane of the earth's path at high angles.

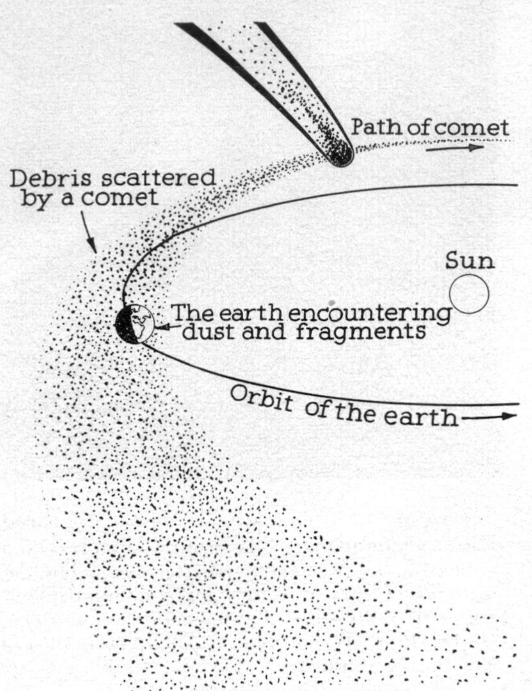

From Davidson : "From Atoms to Stars," by permission of Hutchinson & Co. (Publishers), Ltd.

FIGURE 46. Diagram to show how the earth may encounter dust from the path of a comet.

Some comets return to cross the earth's path at intervals of about the same number of years. Some comets return after a short period, like Encke's which takes $3\frac{1}{2}$ years or Halley's which takes 76 years, while others, according to our calculations, may take hundreds or even thousands of years. We have evidence that some comets break up and finally disappear.

As for the origin of comets, many theories have been put forward, but astronomers are not very satisfied with any of them.

METEORS AND METEORITES

On clear dark nights we may often see a small spot of light rush through part of the sky ; it seems to come from nowhere and to go nowhere and it is all over in the twinkling of an eye. These things are called " shooting stars " or, better, " meteors," for they have nothing to do with the real stars that we see.

Actually they are tiny specks of material which have come off their track into the earth's atmosphere. As they rush into the air round the earth, with terrific speed, they are made white hot by the friction of the air and burn away to the finest powder. Of course, meteors come by day as well as night, as the radio telescopes have recently proved. But our eyes cannot see their feeble track during daylight.

There seems no doubt that some meteors, but by no means all, have come from material left behind by a comet (*not* by a comet's tail) as shown in Figure 46. What can have been the origin of the rest we cannot, at present, surmise.

Meteorites. Sometimes, instead of a tiny particle, there rushes into the earth's atmosphere a lump of matter weighing several pounds, rarely several tons, and, very rarely, hundreds of tons. These are too massive to get entirely burnt up in the air, so they fall on the ground. If you visit the Snowdon region of North Wales, not far away from Snowdon itself at the famous Welsh beauty spot, Beddgelert, you can find the Prince Llewelyn Hotel. A small meteorite weighing 1 pound 12 ounces crashed through the roof of this inn on the night of September 21st, 1949. Half of this meteorite, which is mainly metallic, can be seen in the Natural History Museum at South Kensington, London.

Now look at Figures 47 and 48. The first of these photographs, taken in 1928, shows some of the trees blown down by a great meteorite which had fallen in Siberia twenty years before and had made the crater

Courtesy of the "American Weekly," New York

FIGURE 47. These trees were felled by the blast of the giant meteorite which fell in Siberia in 1908.

shown in the second picture. Fortunately the region was wild and uninhabited and the nearest village was a hundred miles away. There the inhabitants had seen an enormous flash of light and had felt a rush of wind so strong that it had lifted cattle and carts into

FIGURE 48. Professor Kulik taking a photograph at the edge of the main crater formed by the meteorite.

Courtesy of the "American Weekly," New York

the air and carried them for yards. It is true that on the same date what was thought to have been an earthquake shock was registered at places hundreds of miles away. But in 1908 there was no radio, and communications in that part of Siberia hardly existed, so the story of the villagers was dismissed as unlikely. But gradually people believed that it might be true and that is why, in the summer of 1928, two Russian professors struggled for weeks through untrodden virgin forest and mosquito swamps to try to solve the mystery.

We now know that similar great meteorites, some even larger, have fallen in various parts of the world in the past. Figure 49 is a photograph of part of the Chubb crater in northern Quebec which recently has been shown to be meteoric in origin. But the Siberian one of 1908 is still the only one of which we know the date of arrival.

FIGURE 49. Dr. V. B. Meen and Dr. I. W. Jones, two Canadian scientists, standing on the rock-strewn rim of the two-mile-wide crater in Quebec, believed to have been caused by a giant meteor between 30 and 150 centuries ago. The crater, now filled with a lake, has a depth of more than 1000 feet.

Where do such great meteorites come from? We do not know. Many suggestions have been put forward, such as the result of collision between planetoids. Until more knowledge has been obtained astronomers cannot do more than make guesses.

SOME THINGS YOU MAY CARE TO DO

1. Perhaps your teacher will divide the class into small groups for the special study of (*a*) the planetoids, (*b*) various famous comets, (*c*) famous meteorites including those which caused the craters in Siberia and Arizona. If so, every group should produce large coloured diagrams for fixing on the blackboard with Sellotape when the talk to the class is given.

The *Oxford Junior Encyclopaedia*, Volume III, and other books of reference will help you.

2. Visit your local museum and see if there are any specimens of stony meteorites, which are more common than metallic ones.

3. From *Whitaker's Almanack* discover the dates on which you should look out for showers of meteors.

4. If you live near London you should make a special visit to the Mineral Gallery of the Natural History Museum at South Kensington. Its collection of meteorites must be one of the best in the world.

5. Turn to your school or library copy of *Whitaker's Almanack* and read what is given there about meteorites and meteoric dust. Different items of interest are given in different years, so back copies are also useful.

Problem D : **WHAT SHOULD WE KNOW ABOUT STARS ?**

Nowadays astronomers know so much about the stars, and are so rapidly finding out so much more, that the ordinary person is bound to feel very ignorant. And it is probably impossible for him to keep up to date, even with radio and television to help him.

Still there are certain things that we ought to know because they affect the way we think about life as a whole. For instance, we need to know that the universe is far, far more immense than our grandfathers ever dreamed that it could be. Light travels at the stupendous speed of 186,000 miles a *second*, so that in an *hour* it travels more than 600 million miles. The distance that it travels in a *year* is called a light year. Yet on page 53 you read of photographs of stars as far as 500 million light years away from us! Recently Dr. W. Baade of the Mount Wilson and Palomar Observatories has concluded that there are stars at a distance of about 2000 million light years from us.

How do astronomers find out such things ? The full answer to that question is so complicated that few of us would understand it. But we can at least know what are the instruments that scientists use and what are their methods.

FIGURE 50. A night view of the 200-inch Hale telescope at Mount Palomar. Its shutter is open.

Courtesy Mount Wilson & Palomar Observatories

Question 1. **How do men find out about the Stars?**

We have read that the Chinese were studying the sky in a scientific way as long as 6000 years ago. It may be that even before then astronomy was already a serious study. Any attempt to record the passing of time brings in the movements of sun and moon and stars, so every civilization *had* to study the sky. The fact that the circle is divided into 360 degrees is due to early attempts in the Middle East to find the number of days in a year. Can you find out which of the Near East peoples were responsible for this?

It is obvious that all attempts to measure require instruments of measurement. But it is not so obvious *how* to start. Certainly all attempts to fix the length of the year required some measurements regarding some of the fixed stars. Can you suggest what facts might be helpful in this matter?

Of course the Chinese must have had their measuring instruments, thousands of years before Christ. But China was cut off from Western civilization and their knowledge therefore did not pass to the Egyptians or the Greeks. So these people had to invent their own instruments.

As far as one can tell, it was a Greek scientist Aristarchus of Samos who was the first to suggest, about 280 B.C., that the earth and the planets were all going round the sun. Yet almost all of the Greek astronomers for hundreds of years believed that the sun and moon and planets were all going round the earth. Was any part of that idea true?

When, after about A.D. 1400, Western European scientists started again to make measurements of movements of the heavenly bodies they had to start almost from the beginning again.

Even Kopernik, the Polish monk who measured the movements of the planets for years and years and then proved by mathematics that they and the earth were all going round the sun, had only very simple apparatus. In order to have two fixed lines, against which to record the times and positions of the planets as they passed, he cut a slit in the wall of his house.

Look at Figure 43 and see what takes the place of the slit which Kopernik used. Is this slit in a fixed direction or can it be moved and, if so, how ?

Kopernik was not quite right—can you remember what was wrong about his conclusion ? Actually he was perfectly accurate in his reasoning and in his calculations. It was his measurements which were at fault and that was because he did not possess instruments that were very precise.

It was Tycho Brahe the Dane, sometimes called "the father of accurate astronomical observation," who made the first instruments that improved upon the measurements of Kopernik. And it was these measurements that enabled Kepler, the German scientist, to discover how the earth and the planets actually *do* move. Can you remember what that discovery was ? But even Tycho Brahe worked without a telescope : why was that ?

It was Galileo, the great Italian scientist of the University of Padua, who enabled the greatest advances in astronomical measurement to take place. By arranging a converging lens and a diverging lens so that rays of light concentrated by the converging lens are caused by the diverging lens to spread before entering the eye, he produced considerable magnification of a distant object. (Unit 7 : HEARING AND SEEING explains this more fully.) This is the principle employed in making opera glasses, in which someone in a theatre looks at

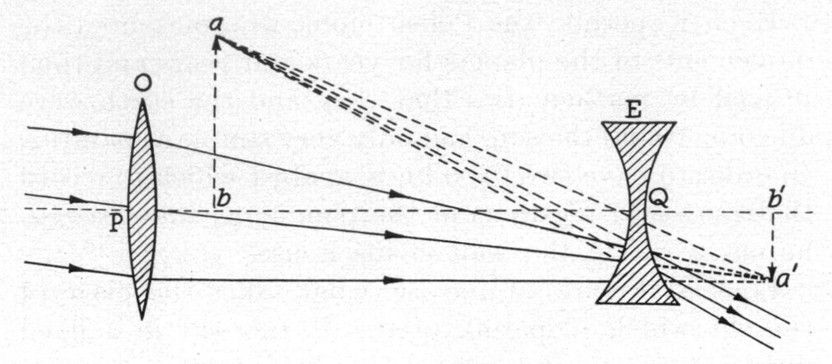

From Duncan & Starling: "A Text Book of Physics," by permission of Macmillan & Co., Ltd.

FIGURE 51. Diagram to show how a Galilean telescope works. The image we see is *ab*.

the singer or actor on the stage. This combination of lenses is usually known as the Galilean telescope.

It is possible, however, to get considerably greater magnification by using two converging lenses as shown in Figure 52 and this is the principle of the ordinary astronomical telescope today.

All sorts of difficulties arise, however, as we try to make lenses which are stronger and larger. So, for the biggest telescopes in the world, that of 100-inch diameter at Mount Wilson and that of 200-inch diameter on Mount Palomar, the magnification is obtained by the use not of lenses but of mirrors.

The idea of using mirrors in making a telescope was

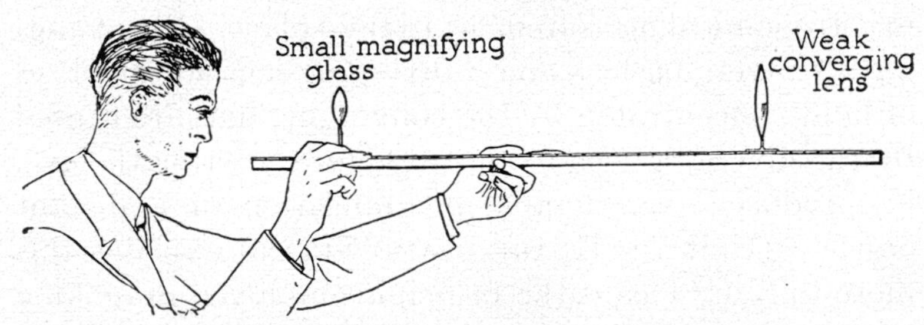

FIGURE 52. How to make a telescope with two simple lenses.

thought out by Isaac Newton. So the new mirror telescope recently installed at the Royal Greenwich Observatory, now at Hurstmonceaux in Sussex, is appropriately named the Isaac Newton telescope. Newton claimed that he saw, and showed to his friends, the phases of Venus with the first quite small mirror telescope. The principal mirror in a Newtonian, or reflector, telescope is paraboloidal, i.e. it is like the mirror in floodlighting equipment, or in a motor-car headlight. But it is used in exactly the opposite way. In floodlighting the lamp is placed at the focal point of the paraboloidal mirror and a parallel beam of light is thrown out by the mirror. (See Figure 53.) In the Newtonian telescope parallel beams of light come from the distant star or planet and are brought to a focus, i.e. a lot of faint light is concentrated at a point. (See Figure 54.) So the wider the mirror the more the light

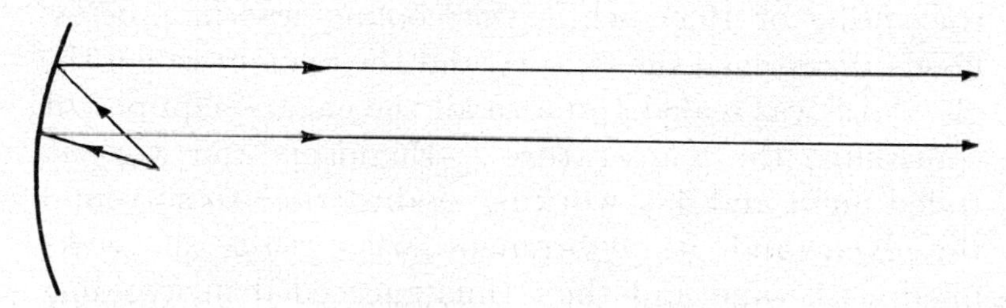

FIGURE 53. In floodlighting or car headlamps light at the focal point is reflected, in parallel rays by the parabolic reflector.

FIGURE 54. Here parallel rays of light from a distant object are all brought to the same point—the focus of the parabolic reflector.

that can be brought in to aid us to see distant stars. That was why a great American astronomer, Dr. Hale, who had already done wonderful things with the huge 100-inch telescope at Mount Wilson, set out towards the end of his life to raise money for one twice as large, the one that now bears his name at Mount Palomar. Both these giant telescopes are situated on mountains in Southern California in the United States, because the dry clear atmospheric conditions there were the best that could be found.

The making of this Hale telescope took nearly fifteen years of concentrated work. Great crucibles of molten pyrex glass were poured every two minutes into a special oven, then unexpectedly the metal supports melted, and a new attempt was made that took a year. Hermetically sealed the disc took ten months to cool at a fixed slow rate accurately regulated. Then in the spring of 1935, while the cooling was in process, floods threatened the factory and the oven in which the glass disc was sealed and also all the electric equipment controlling the temperature! Engineers and workers toiled night and day working against time to surround the oven and its equipment with walls of sacks filled with sand and they thus succeeded in avoiding disaster.

If you think about the making of this mirror, you will realize how astronomical progress was dependent on progress in glassmaking. A few years later, the astounding discoveries made with the two giant telescopes (see page 94 and Figure 66) were only possible because a new kind of extra sensitive photographic plate had been invented. Now, as you will read on page 86, scientists are trying to do still more remarkable things with the incredibly faint rays that large telescopes concentrate into points of light. These latest

Courtesy Mount Wilson & Palomar Observatories

FIGURE 55. The 200-inch Hale telescope on Mount Palomar. This shows the observer sitting in a cage at the focus of the 200-inch reflecting surface.

advances spring from the science of electronics, which is only in its infancy. So great surprises probably still lie ahead.

Radio Telescopes

But in addition to telescopes through which we can look, and telescopes used mainly for taking long exposure photographs, we now have " radio telescopes " which record the presence of bodies which may not be giving out light. If you turn back to the frontispiece you will see the picture of what is, in 1958, the world's largest radio telescope.

It consists of a great paraboloidal bowl, of 250 feet diameter, carried on two steel towers at a height of

Keystone Press Agency, Ltd.

FIGURE 56. The radio telescope erected at Bonn in Germany in 1956. The diameter of the bowl is 83 feet. Compare this with the diameter of the bowl at Jodrell Bank.

about 170 feet above the ground. This is approximately the height of the Nelson column in London. At the top of the towers are laboratories and in these are installed electric motors of 100 horse-power which regulate the upward and downward tilt of the giant bowl. Each tower is carried on six bogies which run on a double railway track of gauge 17 feet. The driving is again done by electric motors of 100 horse-power. In this way the bowl is moved horizontally and the combination of this movement with the vertical movement between the towers enables the bowl to be directed to any part of the sky that the astronomer in control desires.

The circle of the railway track has a diameter of 350 feet and the whole giant instrument is supported by very deep foundations. Indeed it was necessary to sink very long piles of reinforced concrete which extend underground from 45 feet in depth up to 90 feet in depth. In the making of the foundations and the central support-block more than 10,000 tons of steel and concrete were used. The total weight supported by this block is about 2000 tons. The bowl, together with the back girder, weighs 700 tons. The focus of this great bowl, at which the dipole is placed for the reception of radio-waves, is at $62\frac{1}{2}$ feet from the deepest point of the bowl.

One other important point about the construction of this huge instrument concerns the effect upon it of heavy winds. Even in the calmest central regions of the British Isles the wind speed is greater than 15 miles per hour for one third of the hours of any year. At the height of 170 feet the wind speed exceeds 20 miles per hour for more than one third of the time. So the construction had to be such that such a pressure of wind could not, to any important extent, distort the shape of the bowl. Moreover, in times of very violent winds or blizzards it is necessary for the bowl to be inverted and machinery for doing this quickly had to be installed.

Finally, complex electronic calculating machines play a leading part in controlling the motion of this vast bowl.

Radio telescopes of this shape were pioneered at Jodrell Bank as early as 1947, but they are now to be found in a number of countries. Ordinary telescopes need clear skies and clear air and that is why great optical telescopes have to be placed on mountains in dry regions. But for radio telescopy these things are not necessary, so advanced astronomical work can now be done in many parts of the world where, till recently, it was very difficult.

This work of radio astronomy began in 1931 when an American radio engineer called Jansky, having tuned his aerial to a 15-metre waveband, noticed a continual irregular background noise. Further investigation showed that this was coming from all regions of the sky but mostly from the region of the centre of the Milky Way.

If aerials are directed, like telescopes, not towards stars, but towards space between stars, radio signals can still be received. One can imagine the surprise of the scientists who first found this. Still more surprised were they when they were able to prove that the radio waves came from point sources, just as though from stars which had been blacked out. These point sources are now known as "radio stars," and we have little precise idea as yet how numerous they are, or indeed, what they are. One worker believes that, in the region of the Milky Way in which the solar system is found, these stars are 30 times as numerous as ordinary or "optical" stars.

But there may prove to be many different kinds of radio stars, some completely invisible and others which can be associated with known objects. For example, one point source seems to correspond with the Crab Nebula, which is believed to be the expanding shell of gas left by a star that was seen to explode in A.D. 1054. (As this nebula is 4100 light years distant, you can work out the year B.C. when the explosion actually occurred.) But this study of radio stars is only at its beginning and it is going to be an exciting story for you to follow in the years ahead.

Radio telescopes need not necessarily be of the type at Jodrell Bank. At Cambridge University and in other places another type of instrument has been developed. The plan of this type of instrument is to convey to the same receiver two radio waves one of which is arriving at a very small interval of time after the other. From the " interference " which results scientists have been able to discover facts about the radiations from sun-spots and to locate the positions of radio stars with very great accuracy.

The Cambridge instrument, shown in Figure 57, consists of four long aerials connected to a single receiver. The total collecting surface is about one acre, which is about the same as in the instrument at Jodrell Bank. The four aerials are arranged as shown in Figure 58, and in the photograph, Figure 57 (which was taken from position P), you can see three of these aerials. Each aerial is rather like a popular type of electric fire which has a hot bar running along the focus of a parabolic cylindrical reflector. The reflector in the Cambridge instrument is made of long stretched wires with

FIGURE 57. A view of part of the Cambridge University radio telescope.

Courtesy of Dr. Smith, Cavendish Laboratory, Cambridge

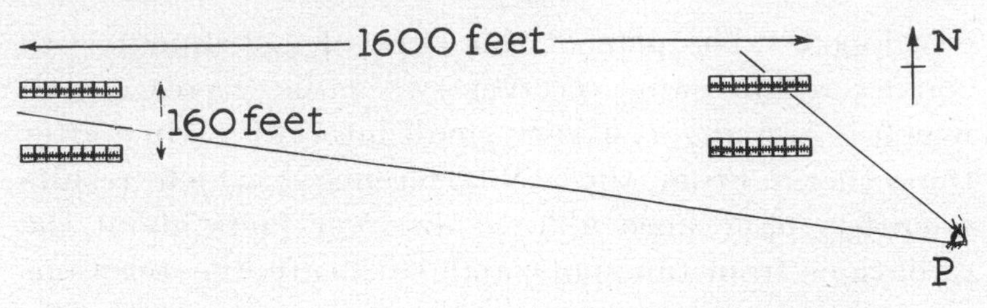

FIGURE 58. This shows you how the four long lines of aerials are arranged and the direction from which the photographs of Figure 57 was taken.

a line of dipoles along the focal line to collect the reflected radiations. This instrument, which first worked on a wavelength of 3·7 metres, detected and located no less than 2000 radio stars—about as many as there are ordinary stars which can be seen with the naked eye.

Radio Telescopes and Comets and Meteors

Radio telescopes are likely to be of great help in solving some of the mysteries about comets and meteors. Briefly we can say that the radio telescope method of studying near objects is to send out radio waves and to detect unseen bodies by the " echo " of the radio wave if it strikes a body of any kind. By this method it is possible to search for meteor activity not merely on clear nights, when tracks might be visible, but also by day, whether fine or cloudy. From this form of study all sorts of new knowledge is coming to hand and you will probably want to keep a notebook in which you can make entries as the years go by.

Before radio astronomy existed calculations had already shown that the number of meteors that enter the earth's atmosphere every 24 hours, and which under suitable conditions could be seen, must be several millions. Thanks to radio astronomy we now know that the number entering our atmosphere every 24 hours must be some thousands of millions! Luckily they are almost all very, very small and a day's delivery into the earth's atmosphere probably amounts to only about one ton.

"*Electronic Telescopes*"

The photograph in Figure 63, of the Nebula in the Hunting Hounds, was taken with an exposure of 10 hours 45 minutes. Most observation of distant stars is done with long exposure photographs because the photographic plate is capable of collecting the accumulated effect of very faint light while the human eye would not respond at all to light so feeble.

But photographic plates, too, have limits to their capacity. The most sensitive plates are too sensitive to be exposed for long hours because the minute grains of silver salt begin to blacken without exposure to light. On the other hand the plates which can be exposed for hours are not as sensitive as astronomers would wish. To affect the minute silver salt grains on such plates 1000 of the units of light known as *photons* must fall upon each grain.

But many years ago scientists found that photographic plates are far more sensitive to *electrons* than to light. Electrons are minute particles from atoms and electricity can be thought of as a stream of electrons. Also there are certain metals, such as caesium and antimony, which give off electrons when very thin layers of them are exposed to light. Every photon of light causes one electron to be set free. So in many countries scientists have been trying to construct instruments that will make light from distant stars expel electrons from metals in such a way as to produce an astronomical photograph.

Recently two French scientists, Lallemand and Duchesne, have succeeded in making an instrument in which one out of every four electrons produced by light from the stars affects a photographic plate. This means that four photons of light now have the same effect on a photographic plate as used to need one thousand photons. In other words, if this apparatus is fixed to a telescope, it multiplies the photographic power of the telescope by 250. As there are still some practical problems not completely solved the multiplying power of the instrument shown in Figure 59 is between 30 and 40. This is equivalent to multiplying the diameter of a telescope's mirror or lens by about 6. So using the telescope of diameter 1·2 metres (how many inches is this ?) at the Saint Michel Observatory, French scientists have taken photographs which, they claim, would have required an ordinary telescope of nearly 280 inches diameter, i.e. a larger telescope than the giant Hale telescope on Mount Palomar.

FIGURE 59. The Lalleman-Duchesne electronic instruments fitted to a telescope in a French observatory.

Courtesy of Professor Duchesne

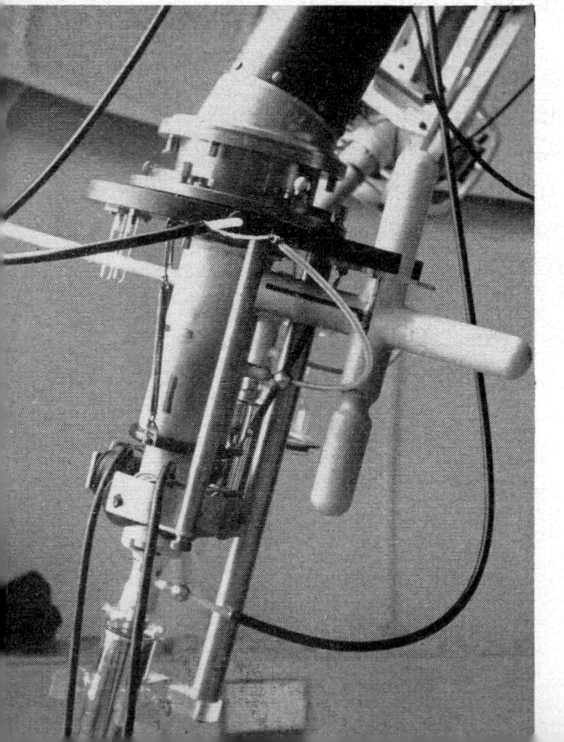

If this type of electronic attachment to telescopes can be shown to be successful and can be widely used it will result in rapid increase in our knowledge. Can you invent a name which would be more accurate than *electronic telescope* ?

1. Make a telescope of your own.

You can make a telescope for yourself from some spare pieces of wood, strong brown paper, a thick wooden pole, and two simple lenses that can be bought from an optical instrument shop.

The first thing to do is to make the tube of the telescope with several sheets of strong brown paper. Make sure that the creases are out of the paper by damping it slightly with a sponge, then take one sheet of paper and wrap it once round the pole, which should be about three feet long and at least two inches in diameter. Hold the paper in place and spread gum or glue over the rest of the paper with a large brush. When you have done this, wind the rest of that sheet of paper round the pole so that none of the gummed side of the paper shows any longer. Now glue several more sheets of brown paper in the same manner round the first sheet and put the pole, with the several layers of paper glued around it, away to dry. When it is thoroughly dry, withdraw the pole and you will have left a strong, hard tube of brown paper.

You will now need your lenses, one large and one small. If you tell the dealer you want them for a telescope, he will sell you two suitable ones, but make sure the diameter of the larger lens does not exceed the *inside* diameter of the tube. Ask the dealer the focal length of each lens and note this down carefully. You will have to cut the tube you have made to the same length as the focal length of the larger of the two lenses. For example, if the focal length of the larger lens is 24 inches, the tube must be 24 inches long.

The larger lens must now be fitted into the end of the tube. If it is a little too small, line the inside of the tube with some brown paper, until there is no gap between the edge of the lens and the inside of the tube. To fix the lens into position, cut out two pieces of fairly thick cardboard about one inch across and long enough to go round the inside of the tube. Take one piece of card and bend it into a circle and then glue it into position about three inches in from the end of the tube, so as to form a support for the lens. Now put in the lens and fix it into place with the other piece of cardboard which has also been made into a ring. This second ring should not be glued in, for you may need to take out the lens from time to time for cleaning.

The smaller lens needs a second tube, made in the same way as the first one, except that a piece of pole the same diameter as the smaller lens should be used to wrap the paper around. When this tube is made, the lens is fixed in the end in the same manner as in the larger tube, but much nearer the end as it will be the eye-piece of your telescope. At the other end of this narrower tube, glue a disc of wood with a very small hole drilled in its exact centre.

Now it only remains to fasten the two tubes together. Take a piece of the thick wooden pole, thick enough to fit tightly inside the larger tube, and drill a hole through the centre large enough for the smaller tube to slide through. Glue this piece of pole inside the open end of the large tube, slide the smaller tube through the pole, into the larger tube, and the telescope is ready for use.

2. A group of the class could work together on a project tracing the development of astronomical measuring apparatus. Names of people you will need to study include Kopernik, Tycho Brahe, Kepler, Galileo, Newton, Flamsteed, William Halley, William Herschel, Bessel, Strave, Hale, and Schmidt.

3. Organize a class *symposium* on " important

observatories of the world," in which each member of the group finds out and talks about an observatory in a different country.

4. In a similar way organize a symposium on " radio telescopes of the world."

5. Make a book of cuttings from newspapers and magazines regarding telescopes, radio telescopes and electronic telescopes and the latest discoveries made by them. It is very important to have such a cutting book, because new facts are being discovered so fast that ordinary books soon become partly out of date.

6. If you and some of your friends have become interested in astronomy, why not form a school Astronomical Society for regular meetings and, perhaps, observations too ? It is possible for your society, or your school, to become affiliated to the British Astronomical Association, a body which has a membership of about 2500 amateur astronomers. Further information can be obtained from the B.A.A., 309 Bath Road, Hounslow West, Middlesex. Membership of the B.A.A. gives the right to borrow books, lantern slides, and, under certain conditions, even telescopes and other apparatus.

7. Probably you would like to know about astronomical films and filmstrips which can be hired and about books and periodicals which will enable you to deepen your knowledge of astronomy. You will find such information in *Teaching Astronomy in Schools* by E. A. Beet, B.Sc. (Cambridge University Press). This valuable little book also gives you detailed descriptions of simple observational work that you can carry on in the open air. *A Guide to the Sky* (Cambridge University Press), by the same author, gives you a simple and delightful introduction to the constellations.

Question 2. **What is the Milky Way ?**

If on a clear dark night you look up at the sky, you can see, stretching right across the heavens, a belt of fuzziness which looks like a mass of distant stars few of which you can distinguish properly. This belt, which we call the Milky Way, goes " right round the earth " in the sense that the same sort of crowded fuzzy track can also be seen from anywhere in the southern hemisphere.

Moreover, in this case our eyes have *not* deceived us : the fuzziness *is* due to countless stars all at a very great distance from us.

These stars that look so distant from us are part of the same system of stars that we can see with our naked eye—some two thousand is commonly reckoned as the number that a person with average sight can clearly distinguish. The total number of stars in our

FIGURE 60. A photograph of a nebular region in Cepheus showing vast numbers of stars which give the cloudy effect.
Courtesy Yerkes Observatory

system, including those that seem so closely packed in the Milky Way, is in the region of 100,000 million!

These stars of our own system, astronomers now tell us, are scattered at great distances apart, but the whole group makes up a bun-like outline in space 100,000 light years across. It is thickest in the centre (20,000 light years) but tapers very much at the edges.

In this mighty group, which is spinning, the sun is situated nearer to the edge than to the centre, as shown in Figure 61. When we, being near the sun, look at the Milky Way, we are really looking in the direction of the edges of this bun. Since we are looking in the direction of the *length* of this bun we see vast numbers of stars which lie in front of others which are in front of still others and so on. No wonder the Milky Way is fuzzy!

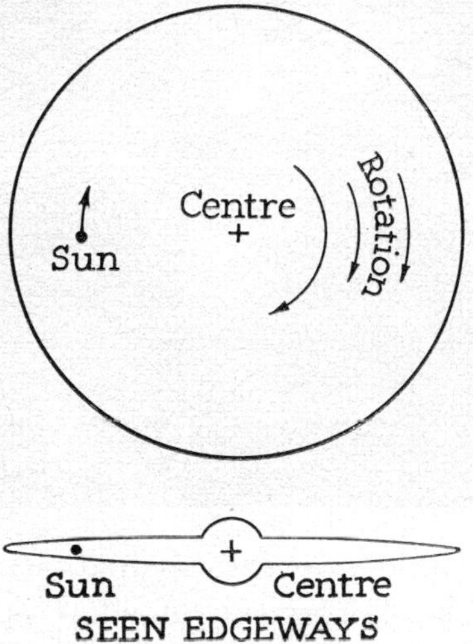

From Davidson: "Astronomy for Everyman," by permission of J. M. Dent & Sons, Ltd.

FIGURES 61 AND 62. These diagrams show the shape and nature of the island Universe to which the sun belongs and which we call the Milky Way.

In addition to the stars in the Milky Way system, there are also scattered atoms and molecules of hydrogen and other elements, and what is called "inter-stellar dust." Where clouds of this material collect, the passage of light from the stars is blocked, and sometimes under certain conditions the clouds send out radio waves which we are now able to pick up with the new radio telescopes.

There is another important point which astronomers

Courtesy Mount Wilson Observatory

FIGURE 63. This spiral nebula is another galaxy of millions of stars. The back endpaper of this book shows another spiral nebula. If there is any observer with a telescope anywhere in that galaxy, he will see our Milky Way as a spiral nebula.

have now established. Look at Figure 63, which shows a photograph of what is called a spiral *nebula* (this is the Latin word for *cloud*). This nebula is in fact another system of millions of stars, just like our Milky Way system, and we are gradually accumulating evidence that our system, too, has spiral arms like the nebula in the photograph. It is thought that our sun is in one of the spiral arms of the Milky Way system.

A group of hundreds of millions of stars swirling along together, like the group to which our sun belongs, is called a *Galaxy*. This word really means a " Milky Way " and had to be invented when astronomers found that our Milky Way is not the only one in the universe. In fact, outside our galaxy, at unimaginable distances apart, lie more galaxies, tens of millions of them, more or less of a similar shape to ours, though many of them are much smaller.

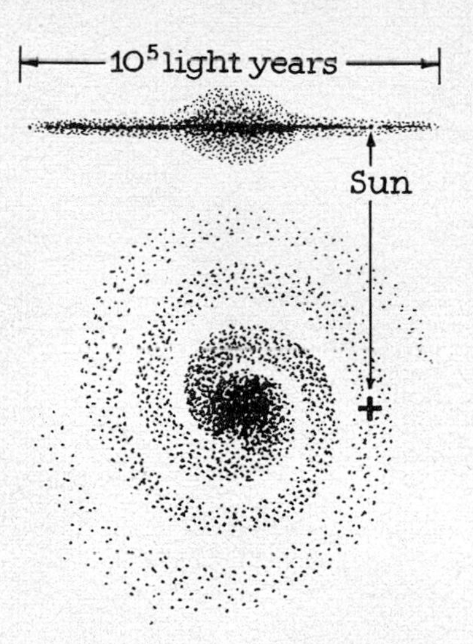

Based on Fig. 1·5 in Ellison: "The Sun and its Influence," by permission of Routledge & Kegan Paul, Ltd.

FIGURE 64. This diagram shows how the sun is placed in one of the spiral arms of the Milky Way.

Even the wonders of spiral galaxies, however, must not lead us to think that all things can be explained in terms of spirals. For the great telescopes have recently shown us that there are galaxies which are irregular and galaxies which are elliptical. Some astronomers at present think that galaxies may begin as irregular ones, then, gradually over vast periods of time, become spiral, and then after hundreds or thousands of millions of years become elliptical.

Look now at Figure 65 which shows us a photograph of the Great Nebula in the constellation Andromeda—a nebula which one can just detect with the naked eye. It is relatively " near " to us compared with other nebulas beyond our own system. Yet this nebula is reckoned to be well over one million light years away from us. This is another galaxy, a very large one, with hundreds of millions of stars of its own! But we are seeing it " end-on," looking at the rim, as it were, whereas in Figure 63 we are seeing a spiral full face. We now know that the Andromeda galaxy is spinning, but it is thought to take more than 60 million years to complete one turn. So an astronomer cannot hope to see very much movement in his lifetime!

Courtesy Mount Wilson & Palomar Observatories

FIGURE 65. This is a photograph of the Great Nebula in Andromeda and it shows the spiral arms. Special photographs have shown that the central cloud of this nebula is a vast number of separate stars.

It was the 100-inch telescope of Mount Wilson which has enabled us to know that the centre of this nebula is not, as used to be thought, a cloud of luminous gas. If you look at old photographs of this nebula a central cloudy mass is exactly what you see. But during the Second World War, Dr. Baade at Mount Wilson took long-exposure photographs with special plates sensitive to red light. These photographs showed the central cloud resolved into a vast number of separate stars.

This, of course, greatly changed our ideas about nebulas and the central parts of many other nebulae have now been resolved into separate stars. (See Figure 66.) Astronomers have recently discovered that the brightest stars in the central region of the

Courtesy Mount Wilson & Palomar Observatories

FIGURE 66. This photograph shows what is seen when the fuzzy portion of a nebula is resolved into separate stars by photographing with plates sensitive to red light. It is the centre of the Nebula in Andromeda and was taken with the 200-inch telescope at Mount Palomar.

Andromeda nebula are " cool " red stars. But these, on the average, are about 1000 times as bright as our sun.

In the region of our own galaxy in which the sun is found, the brightest stars are very hot blue stars more than 100,000 times as bright as the sun!

Probably all these vast figures of enormous distances and unimaginable periods of time make your head whirl. Do not be disappointed with yourself if this is the case: even astronomers find themselves bewildered by the astonishing revelations that their science brings them.

In Unit One you read of the Way of a Scientist. You there read of the patient and extremely exact way in which a scientist must work, not asking for quick results, not rushing to conclusions in the absence of evidence, plodding steadily day by day, obeying the rules of scientific thought. A scientist is never ashamed to say, "I do not know." That is the answer of the astronomer to many of the questions that we would want to ask him. Astronomers know well how great is the power of the human mind, and how a team of people can often resolve the most baffling problem. But they also know the limitations of the human mind, and so they are humble men. But whether scientists study the infinitely small, such as the atom and its structure, or the infinitely large, such as the universe and its nature, every step reveals something more and more wonderful, more and more complicated, more and more difficult to understand.

Will future scientists find a key to any one of the many riddles of the universe that baffle us today? Or will their work merely increase the number of unsolved problems? It is amazing how much an animal, about six feet tall and living for less than a century, has already found out about astronomical periods of time calculated in millions of years and about astronomical distances calculated in millions of light years. But every true scientist knows how much he does not know.